Little Voices
Showtunes

Published by
Novello Publishing Limited
14-15 Berners Street, London, W1T 3LJ, UK.

Exclusive distributors:
Music Sales Limited
Distribution Centre, Newmarket Road, Bury St Edmunds, Suffolk, IP33 3YB, UK.

Music Sales Pty Limited
120 Rothschild Avenue, Rosebery, NSW 2018, Australia.

Order No. NOV940687 ISBN 978-1-84772-168-6
This book © Copyright 2007 Novello & Company Limited.

Arranged by Barrie Carson Turner.
Edited by Rachel Payne.
Music processed by Paul Ewers Music Design.

Printed in the EU.

www.musicsales.com

NOVELLO PUBLISHING LIMITED
part of The Music Sales Group
London / New York / Paris / Sydney / Copenhagen / Berlin / Madrid / Tokyo

Track Listing

1. Food, Glorious Food (from 'Oliver!')
(Bart) Lakeview Music Publishing Company Limited
Full Performance

2. Bad Guys (from 'Bugsy Malone')
(Williams) Chappell Music Limited
Full Performance

3. Joseph's Dreams (from 'Joseph And
His Amazing Technicolor® Dreamcoat')
(Rice/Lloyd Webber) The Really Useful Group
Full Performance

4. The Rhythm Of Life (from 'Sweet Charity')
(Fields/Coleman) Campbell Connelly & Company Limited
Full Performance

5. Hakuna Matata
(from Walt Disney Pictures' 'The Lion King')
(John/Rice) Warner Chappell Artemis Music
Full Performance

6. Food, Glorious Food (from 'Oliver!')
(Bart) Lakeview Music Publishing Company Limited
Piano Accompaniment

7. Bad Guys (from 'Bugsy Malone')
(Williams) Chappell Music Limited
Piano Accompaniment

8. Joseph's Dreams (from 'Joseph And
His Amazing Technicolor® Dreamcoat')
(Rice/Lloyd Webber) The Really Useful Group
Piano Accompaniment

9. The Rhythm Of Life (from 'Sweet Charity')
(Fields/Coleman) Campbell Connelly & Company Limited
Piano Accompaniment

10. Hakuna Matata
(from Walt Disney Pictures' 'The Lion King')
(John/Rice) Warner Chappell Artemis Music
Piano Accompaniment

Food, Glorious Food

from Oliver!

Words & Music by Lionel Bart

2.

gru - el! There's not a crust; not a crumb can we find, can we

Still we get the same old gru - el; not a crumb can we find, can we

Fmaj7   Bb/F   Fmaj7

beg, can we bor-row or cadge. But there's no - thing to stop us from

beg, can we bor-row or cadge.

F7   Bb/F   F   Fm6

Three ban-quets a day: our fa-vour - ite di - et!_____
that ex - tra bit more? That's all that we live for._____

Three ban-quets a day, this is our, our fa-vour - ite di - et!
that, that lit - tle ex - tra bit more, that's all that we live for.

C   Gm7   C7   F   Dm/F   G7

Just pic - ture a great big steak; fried roast-ed or stewed! Oh,
Why should we be fat - ed to do no-thing but brood on

Just pic - ture a great big steak, fried and roast-ed or stewed! Oh,
Why should we be fat - ed to do just no-thing but brood on

C   C#dim   Dm   G7   Am   D7   Ab7

9

Bad Guys

from Bugsy Malone

Words & Music by Paul Williams

11

Bad guys.___ We're the ve - ry worst, each of us con-tempt-i - ble, we're

Bad guys.___ We're the ve - ry worst, con-tempt-i - ble, we're

cri - ti - cised and cursed. We made the big___ time, ma - li-cious and mad.___

cri - ti - cised and, and cursed. We made the big___ time, ma - li-cious and mad.___

We're the ve-ry best at be-ing bad.

We're the ve-ry best at be-ing bad.

decresc.

We could-'ve been a-ny-thing that we want-ed to be,___ we took the ea-sy way / with all the ta-lent we

We could-'ve been a-ny-thing that we, that we want-ed to be, we took the / with all the

out.
had.
With lit-tle train-ing, we mas-tered com-plain - ing.
With lit-tle prac-tice, we made ev - 'ry black_ list.

ea - sy way out.__
ta-lent we had.__
With lit-tle train-ing, we mas-tered com-plain - ing.
With lit-tle prac-tice, we made ev - 'ry black_ list.

Bm Cdim A/C# D7   G

1.   2.

Man-ners seemed un-ne-ces-sa-ry. We're so rude, it's al-most sca-ry. We're the ve-ry best at be-ing

We're so rude, it's al-most sca-ry. We're the ve-ry best at be-ing

A7/E   A7   D7   C   D7

bad._____ We're the ve - ry best at be - ing bad._____

bad, *oh, so* bad!__ We're the ve - ry best at be - ing bad, *real - ly* bad!__

G F#7 F7 E7   C   D7   G F#7 F7 E7

We're the ve - ry best at be - ing bad.

We're the ve - ry best at be - ing bad.

C   D7   G   D7   G

15

Joseph's Dreams

from Joseph And His Amazing Technicolor® Dreamcoat

Words by Tim Rice
Music by Andrew Lloyd Webber

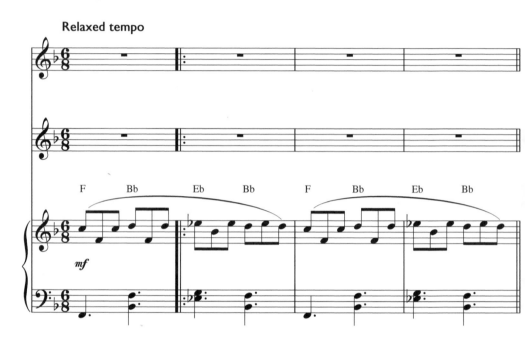

Jo - seph's coat an - noyed his bro - thers, But what makes us mad are the
This is not the kind of thing we bro - thers like to hear, It

things   that   Jo - seph   tells   us   of   the   dreams   he's   of - ten   had.   I
seems   to   us   that   Jo - seph   and   his   dreams   should   dis - ap - pear.   I

things   that   Jo - seph   tells   us   of   the   dreams   he's   of - ten   had.   I
seems   to   us   that   Jo - seph   and   his   dreams   should   dis - ap - pear.   I

dreamed   that   in   the   fields   one   day,   at   corn - col - lect - ing   time,_____
dreamed   I   saw   e - le - ven   stars,   the   sun   and   moon   and   sky,_____

dreamed,_____   I   dreamed,_____   at   corn - col - lect - ing   time,_____   Your
dreamed,_____   I   dreamed,_____   the   sun   and   moon   and   sky,_____   Were

Your e - le - ven sheaves of corn all turned and bowed to mine,_____ My
Bow - ing down be - fore my star, it made me won - der why._____

sheaves_____ of corn_____ all turned and bowed to mine,_____ My
bow - ing down_____ it made me won - der why,_____

Bb   F   C7   F

sheaf was quite a site to see, a gold - en sheaf and
Could it be that I was born for high - er things than

sheaf_____ was quite_____ a gold - en sheaf and
Could_____ I be_____ for high - er things than

Bb   F   C7

18

tall._____ Yours were green and se - cond rate, and
you?_____ A post in some - one's go - vern - ment, a

tall._____ While yours_____ were green,_____ and
you?_____ In go - - vern - ment,_____ a

F   Bb   F

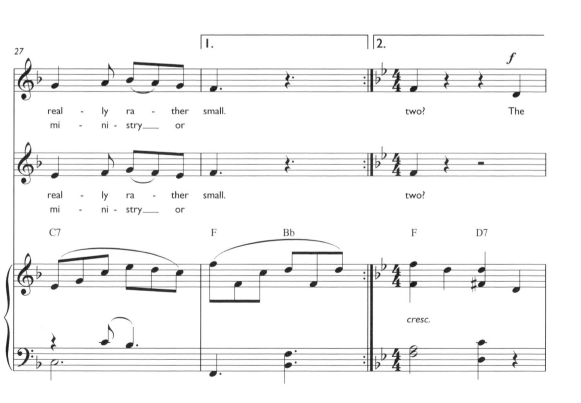

1.   2.   *f*

real - ly ra - ther small.   two?   The
mi - ni - stry____ or

real - ly ra - ther small.   two?
mi - ni - stry____ or

C7   F   Bb   F   D7

cresc.

dreams are more than cry-stal clear,_ the writ - ing on the wall,_

The dreams are cry - stal clear, the writ - ing on the

Gm   Em7b5   Eb   D7   Gm

Means that Jo - seph some day soon_ will rise a - bove us all._ The

wall, Means that he will rise a - bove us all._ The

Gm   Em7b5   Eb   D7   Gm

ac - cu - ra - cy of the dreams_ we bro - thers do not know, But

ac - cu - ra - cy of the dreams_ we bro - thers do_____ not know,

Bb   F/A   Gm   Dsus   D   D7

one thing we are sure a - bout,_ the dream - er has to go._

But this we're sure a - bout,_ the dream - er has to go._

Gm   Em7b5   Eb   D7   Gm

21

The Rhythm Of Life

from Sweet Charity

Words by Dorothy Fields
Music by Cy Coleman

com-mon law wife. Spread the re-li-gion of The Rhy-thm Of Life." And The

wife. And spread The Rhy-thm Of Life."

A7sus/E A7/E Dm Gm6/Bb A7 Dm

Rhy-thm Of Life is a pow-er-ful beat, puts a tin-gle in your fin-gers and a

pow-er-ful beat,

Fm Bbm7 Eb

tin - gle in your feet, rhy - thm in your bed - room,

tin - gle in your feet,

Cm   Ab   Db

rhy-thm in the street, yes The Rhy-thm Of Life is a pow-er-ful beat.

rhy-thm in the street, The Rhy-thm Of Life. To feel The

Bbm   Gm7b5   C   C7sus   Fm

f

f

To feel The Rhy-thm Of Life, to feel the pow-er-ful beat,

Rhy-thm Of Life, to feel the pow-er-ful beat, to feel the

to feel the tin-gle in your fin-gers, to feel the tin-gle in your feet.

tin-gle in your fin-gers, to feel the tin - gle in your feet. To feel The

* slow jazz arpeggios ad lib.

Hakuna Matata

from Walt Disney Pictures' The Lion King

Music by Elton John
Words by Tim Rice

Slowly (relaxed tempo)

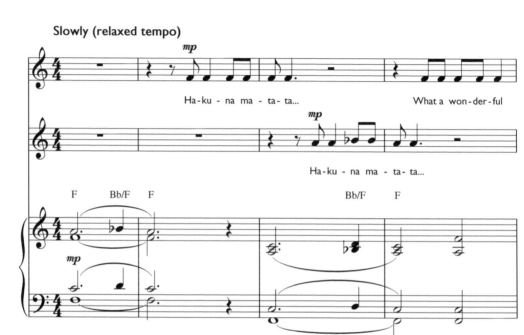

Moderate bouncy shuffle

craze._____ It means no wor - ries for the rest of your days._____

craze._____ It means no wor-ries for the rest of your days._____

G7   Gaug E/G#   Am   D/F#

_____ It's our prob-lem - free_____ phi - lo - so - phy. Ha - ku - na ma-

_____ Yes, it's our prob-lem - free_____ phi - lo - so - phy. Ha - ku - na ma-

D9   C/G   G

19

ta- ta...   what a won-der-ful phrase!_   Ha-ku - na ma

ta- ta...   what a won-der-ful phrase!   What a won-der-ful phrase! Ha-ku - na ma

F   Bb/F   F   C   F/C   C

23

- ta - ta...   ain't no pass - ing craze.   It means no

- ta - ta...   ain't no pass-ing craze.____

F   Bb/F   D7/F#   F#dim   D7/F#   G   C/E

30

wor - ries   for   the   rest of your   days._____   It's   our

It means   no   wor-ries for the rest of your   days._____   It's   our

prob-lem - free_____   phi - lo - so - phy.   Ha - ku - na ma -

prob-lem - free_____   phi - lo - so - phy.   Ha - ku - na ma -

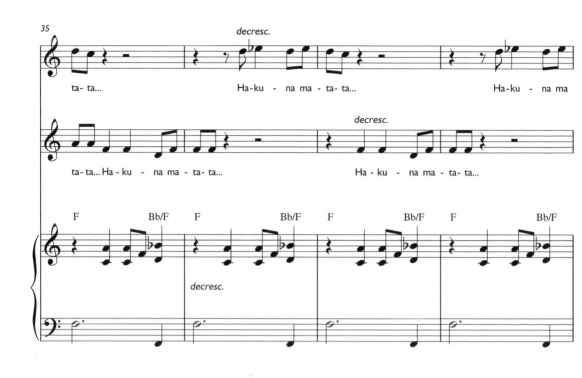

Janu

Day by Day
with
God

Rooting women's lives in the Bible

BRF

BRF

15 The Chambers, Vineyard
Abingdon OX14 3FE
brf.org.uk

Bible Reading Fellowship is a charity (233280)
and company limited by guarantee (301324),
registered in England and Wales

ISBN 978 1 80039 112 3
All rights reserved

This edition © 2021 Bible Reading Fellowship
Cover image © iStock.com/Nikola Ilic

Distributed in Australia by:
MediaCom Education Inc, PO Box 610, Unley, SA 5061
Tel: 1 800 811 311 | admin@mediacom.org.au

Distributed in New Zealand by:
Scripture Union Wholesale, PO Box 760, Wellington
Tel: 04 385 0421 | suwholesale@clear.net.nz

Acknowledgements

Scripture quotations marked with the following abbreviations are taken from the version
shown. Where no abbreviation is given, the quotation is taken from the same version as
the headline reference. NIV: The Holy Bible, New International Version (Anglicised edition)
copyright © 1979, 1984, 2011 by Biblica. Used by permission of Hodder & Stoughton
Publishers, a Hachette UK company. All rights reserved. 'NIV' is a registered trademark
of Biblica. UK trademark number 1448790. MSG: *The Message*, copyright © 1993, 1994,
1995, 1996, 2000, 2001, 2002 by Eugene H. Peterson. Used by permission of NavPress. All
rights reserved. Represented by Tyndale House Publishers, Inc. NLT: The Holy Bible, New
Living Translation, copyright © 1996, 2004, 2007, 2013. Used by permission of Tyndale
House Publishers, Inc., Carol Stream, Illinois 60188. All rights reserved. TPT: The Passion
Translation®. Copyright © 2017, 2018, 2020 by Passion & Fire Ministries, Inc. Used by
permission. All rights reserved. thePassionTranslation.com. ESV: The Holy Bible, English
Standard Version, published by HarperCollins Publishers, © 2001 Crossway Bibles, a division
of Good News Publishers. Used by permission. All rights reserved. VOICE: The Voice Bible
Copyright © 2012 Thomas Nelson, Inc. The Voice™ translation © 2012 Ecclesia Bible Society
All rights reserved.

A catalogue record for this book is available from the British Library

Printed and bound by Gutenberg Press, Tarxien, Malta

Day by Day
with
God

Edited by **Jackie Harris**   **January–April 2022**

Writers in this issue

Rachel Ridler is mum to two energetic boys. She has used BRF's Parenting for Faith resources for many years and began writing for BRF in 2020. She loves exploring the Bible with others online, virtually and in person!

Chris Leonard has been writing for *Day by Day with God* since 1998 and has several books published by BRF. She leads writing groups, creative writing holidays and a church homegroup, and has three young grandchildren.

Rachel Turner is the Parenting for Faith pioneer at BRF (**parentingforfaith.org**) and the author of six books. Over the past 15 years she has worked across a variety of denominations as a children's, youth and family life pastor.

Lyndall Bywater lives in Canterbury and works with The Salvation Army and the Diocese of Canterbury, helping people pray. She is the author of two books, both published by BRF: *Faith in the Making* and *Prayer in the Making*.

Helen Williams has written for BRF since 2016 but has been grateful for its work and presence for a great deal longer. She's married to a bishop in the Anglican Church and spends most of her time engaged in work related to this, while also working part-time as a musician.

Elaine Storkey is an academic, author, broadcaster and senior member of Newnham College, Cambridge. A former president of Tearfund, she also directed the London Institute for Contemporary Christianity for ten years and has taught in universities both in the UK and overseas.

Di Archer is CEO of **tastelifeuk.org**, a charity she co-founded after family experience of eating disorders. An educator, writer and speaker, she is also resources manager on the CPAS Leadership Training team and has written for BRF since 1999.

Annie Willmott has two sons and works for a charity, as a funeral pastor and preaches regularly at her church. She is the author of *Cold Cups of Tea & Hiding in the Loo*. Annie worked for Parenting for Faith at BRF from 2016 to 2019 and has written for them since.

Lakshmi Jeffreys began a church placement with Canon David Winter, then editor of *New Daylight*, in 1993. Twenty years later she delighted in seeing her first notes published in the same series. She combines writing with various other roles within and beyond the church.

Sandra Wheatley has written for BRF since 2000. A former nurse, retirement came early due to the rapid onset of MS. She lives in Newcastle and loves to share God's encouragements through her writing and extensive prayer ministry.

Welcome

It was reading Chris Leonard's study on doorways and gates that reminded me of the inspirational words of Minnie Louise Haskins, so apt for the beginning of a new year: 'And I said to the man who stood at the gate of the year: "Give me a light that I may tread safely into the unknown." And he replied: "Go out into the darkness and put your hand into the hand of God. That shall be to you better than light and safer than a known way." So I went forth, and finding the hand of God, trod gladly into the night.'

Originally written in 1908, these words became both well-known and well-loved after George VI quoted them in his Christmas broadcast in 1939. After our own dark time of crisis, upheaval and change over the last two years, they speak to us again, reminding us that God knows the way ahead and we can trust him to lead us through.

In the years between Minnie writing her poem and its coming to prominence, a new ministry began in 1922, distributing Bible reading notes in Brixton, South London. One hundred years later, BRF is a worldwide ministry, providing resources and encouragement to enable people of all ages to grow in their faith and understanding of the Bible.

Day by Day with God is a part of that ministry and so, whatever else 2022 brings, we want it to be a year of celebration as we thank God for the way he has led us over the years and seek his direction for the future.

As we stand on the threshold of the year, may we encourage you to put your hand into God's hand, knowing that as you prayerfully read his word, it will be for you a lamp for your feet and a light for your path.

Jackie Harris, Editor

Please see pages 136–37 for BRF's specially written Centenary Prayer, and to find out more about our centenary celebrations.

Making Jesus known (lessons from Paul and the early church)

Rachel Ridler writes:

How much do you *really* know about the early church? Maybe, like me, it's been a little while since you last read the book of Acts (or maybe you haven't ventured into this inspiring book of the Bible yet) and pondered what it was like to be in that first class of Christians, putting yourself in their shoes. Doesn't that sound like a great way to kick off this New Year?

The early church were trailblazers. Stepping into the unknown with nothing but their faith in Jesus and an excitement to share that with others to guide them. They didn't have the biographies of Jesus (the gospels) to examine, just the word of mouth that was carrying faster than any news had before. They didn't have books on leadership styles or mission strategies, or even Paul's letters to help them become 'church' (Paul was still figuring it out too!). They just listened to God and followed what they felt called to do.

Brave. Bold. Infectious. They were all these things and more. Isn't that what we all dream to be as Christians? Don't we yearn to be *brave* enough to invite our friends, neighbours and family to hear the gospel? Don't we long to be *bold* and step up to share our stories with those we meet in our day-to-day lives? And wouldn't we shout with joy if those stories were so *infectious* that we saw lives changed and new believers coming to faith?

Well, if that is you, then join me, a flawed and failing 'mum on a mission' from Doncaster, as I seek to be inspired by the early church in making Jesus known this January.

Let's dig into scripture and find out how they *really* shared the gospel, how they authentically started the church as we know it and how we can follow in their footsteps and become trailblazers ourselves. I know I will be putting all of this into action in my day-to-day life as a mum, a church worker and a Christian, and my prayer is that you will do the same.

Confidence in who Jesus is

After his suffering, he presented himself to them and gave many convincing proofs that he was alive. He appeared to them over a period of forty days and spoke about the kingdom of God. (NIV)

After reading the gospel accounts of Jesus' life, I always assumed it would be so clear to the disciples who Jesus is. I mean, they spent the best part of three years with him, watching him perform miracle after miracle, preaching the most amazing sermons on numerous occasions and just generally being the Son of God. And yet, we reach the book of Acts and these men still need 'convincing proofs' for a period of 40 days to fully believe that he was alive.

Maybe we should cut them some slack – it had been a traumatic time, after all – but it does make me feel much happier about my doubts when I read this passage! That the men who knew Jesus best needed extra time to understand and believe before they were thoroughly convinced means that there is hope for me yet. The first ever Christians struggled with doubt, and it's okay if we do too. But they did reach a point where they were convinced and had confidence in who Jesus was and everything he had taught them.

Why is that important? Because if they hadn't reached that point of confidence, they wouldn't have been able to do the work they were called to do – to start the church. The second any persecution or confrontation came their way, they would have been crippled. So before we can start along this journey of making Jesus known and being inspired by these amazing first Christians, we need to first follow their example and become confident in who Jesus is – the Son of God, our Saviour, the Christ.

Today, write down any doubts or questions you have about your faith in Jesus. Ask God to give you convincing proofs about these things or the confidence to accept the unknowable.

RACHEL RIDLER

Infectious excitement

They arrested them and threw them in jail until morning, for by now it was late in the evening. But many of those who listened had already believed the Message – in round numbers about five thousand! (MSG)

'Infectious' is normally a negative term. When used in relation to viruses, the more infectious something is, the more it spreads and the more deadly it could be. Back in 2020, at the height of the coronavirus pandemic, R-rate was the most important number. It was the reproduction rate of the virus. For every person infected, how many others would they infect? If the R number was above one, it meant the virus was growing and the pandemic worsening. If the R number was below one, it meant the virus was dying out – we were beating it!

The R-rate of the early church was phenomenal; in this passage it would have been close to 2,500! For just two men, John and Peter, managed to infect 5,000 people with the good news of Jesus. This is even while being arrested, which wasn't enough to curb their infectious excitement for the message of Christ.

Have we forgotten the power of excitement and how the way we speak about something affects others? Think about the product that someone can't stop talking about, so we buy one too, or the diet that is working wonders for our friend, so we decide to give it a try!

Is that the way we speak about our relationship with God? Do we rave about our church services or tell others about the amazing prayer session we had? When was the last time that others could see our excitement to go to church and felt like they were missing out by not being there? What is our R-rate and how infectious are we with our faith? I think I would be ashamed to share mine with Peter and John. So our next step in becoming like these inspirational men is to recapture our excitement for this God we love and serve.

Are there times when you lack excitement for church life, or when people see negativity instead when you talk about faith? Ask God to build that excitement in your heart for him so that it bubbles out to those around you.

RACHEL RIDLER

Sustaining community

Every day they continued to meet together in the temple courts. They broke bread in their homes and ate together with glad and sincere hearts, praising God and enjoying the favour of all the people. And the Lord added to their number daily those who were being saved. (NIV)

A friend from Africa recently told me about the things she missed from her time living there: your neighbour's house was your house, and eating meals together was normal. Instead of the isolated family unit that we observe here in the UK, they had a more fluid and open way of interacting with each other.

Part of me would love to live like this! I yearn to have closer relationships with my neighbours, but often my fear of breaking our social rules stops me from inviting them round for dinner or saying that the kids can play in our back garden whenever they want.

When I read this passage, I can see that the infectious excitement has now grown into an infectious and buzzing community. These people don't hear the good news of the gospel and run off in wild abandon! No. They gather together and support each other in finding their feet with this life-changing news.

When big news drops, we *need* to talk about it. We need to dissect it and chat it through with those around us. I know when my estate was informed that all our houses were going to be bulldozed to make way for the new high-speed railway, we were out on the streets talking to neighbours we'd never even met, just trying to make sense of it. We forged a new Facebook community so we could discuss the logistics of selling our homes to the government and share news on the subject. It was a natural thing to do – we didn't want anyone to go through it alone.

Where do you go to share good news, figure out your faith or ask questions? Ask God to draw you closer to others so that you can build a community that will sustain you in your Christian journey.

RACHEL RIDLER

Prayer a priority

'Brothers and sisters, choose seven men from among you who are known to be full of the Spirit and wisdom. We will turn this responsibility over to them and will give our attention to prayer and the ministry of the word.' (NIV)

Currently my day job is as a youth, children's and families' worker in a local church. Most days you will find me running groups, preparing activities or delivering assemblies in local schools. There is much to be done and only a limited number of hours in the day. And yet sometimes my mentors and manager have to remind me that prayer is just as valid a work activity in my role as any of those things. It is something I so easily skip over or slip in quickly before the important things on my never-ending to-do list. But it shouldn't be.

The first Christians knew that. They could see the practical tasks starting to take over – quarrels to break up, administration to do, food to be handed out – and realised these concerns were drawing them away from the time they had to devote to prayer and their ministry. So what did they do? They delegated.

Perhaps I need to learn from them and try to delegate more tasks to the volunteers in my team so that I can focus on praying for the children, families and young people I work with. I am certainly questioning whether prayer is a big enough priority in my work life, and my personal life.

What happened when the disciples made this stand and officially made prayer their priority? Well, simply put, their ministry exploded! The numbers becoming Christians grew every day and God heard those prayers. If we want our prayers to be as powerful as theirs, we need to follow their example. This may involve sacrificing something else that we love and want to do – even things that are good and look like ministry.

Father, help us to make prayer a priority in our lives, even when that means sacrificing other good things. Help us to see the power of prayer and to yearn to put it first. Amen

RACHEL RIDLER

Guided by the Holy Spirit

The Holy Spirit said to Philip, 'Go over and walk along beside the carriage.' Philip ran over and heard the man reading from the prophet Isaiah. Philip asked, 'Do you understand what you are reading?' The man replied, 'How can I, unless someone instructs me?' And he urged Philip to come up into the carriage and sit with him. (NLT)

Are you a big party kind of person or a small, simple coffee with a friend kind of person? Maybe, like me, you enjoy both at different times. After all the drama and excitement of the arrival of the Holy Spirit and thousands becoming Christians in those early days, I find great comfort and encouragement from this small story found in the middle of that noise.

Here, we see a completely different side to the Holy Spirit. Perhaps, after all the big moves of the last few weeks, he longs to find respite in the quiet encounters again, in the same way that we need rest after a busy week. What can we learn, then, from Philip and this peaceful meeting? We can follow his example in being ready, being observant, being invited and being understanding.

First, he is ready and willing to follow wherever the Holy Spirit leads. Are we as ready to follow those promptings? Second, he is observant. Yes, the Holy Spirit *leads* him to the carriage, but he doesn't give him step-by-step instructions of why or what to do next. Philip notices the man and gets the picture – this is why he has been led there – and he observes what is needed next. Third, he waits to be invited. Many times, where the Holy Spirit leads, he has already prepared a heart, so the hard work is done. Yes, we should offer an invitation to start a conversation, but then we should wait until the person is ready to invite us in. Finally, Philip is understanding of where that person is at. He doesn't judge this person for not knowing what he is reading but meets him there and helps him to understand more.

Are you ready to follow where the Holy Spirit leads? Pray and ask him to lead you to some quiet encounters with people this week, readying your heart to respond like Philip did.

RACHEL RIDLER

Praise on their lips

About midnight Paul and Silas were praying and singing hymns to God, and the other prisoners were listening to them. (NIV)

I can vividly remember some of the saddest times in my life because of the music that I associate with them. A couple of years ago, I was aware that I was going to be made redundant and had been called down to the head office of the charity I worked for. My brain was swimming with thoughts and my heart beating ten to the dozen, but I clung to the inspirational words of 'I raise a hallelujah', a worship song from Bethel Music, which encourages us to keep singing during our storms.

I imagine that song was heavily inspired by today's verse, and I could have happily sung it on repeat during that season. I drew the lyrics in pictures and stuck them to my wardrobe doors so that I could see them the morning I travelled by train to the meeting. I sung them in my head on the journey and as I walked into the board room. It was the one thing that kept me focused on God during that awful meeting, and without the music my negative thoughts would have taken over.

Music is a powerful thing. We all know how emotive it can be. It should be no surprise then that God chooses to use it as well. I can imagine the swirl of negative thoughts in that prison cell. And yet Paul and Silas chose to silence those thoughts with prayers and with music. The music may have started as a way to drown out the sadness of where they were, but I am sure that the mood and the atmosphere would have changed as soon as they began to sing and God took over!

How can you use music like Paul and Silas to inspire you in tough times and bring your thoughts back to God? Listen to some worship music today and spend time praising God.

RACHEL RIDLER

God on their side

Suddenly an angel of the Lord appeared and a light shone in the cell. He struck Peter on the side and woke him up. 'Quick, get up!' he said, and the chains fell off Peter's wrists. (NIV)

As a mum, sometimes you have to take extreme action to protect your children: quickly grabbing a wrist to pull them away from a road or giving slaps to the back to dislodge something they are choking on. It might seem to the children that their parents are against them, but we know that we are doing it for their own good. Perhaps it's odd that I titled this thought 'God on their side' and yet here is an angel essentially hitting Peter to wake him up! That doesn't sound too nice to me.

But all the way through the book of Acts we see that God is very much on the side of the new Christians, and this is just one example. If Peter had stayed in that prison cell, he would have been tried and most likely killed. Clearly, God had other plans. They might not have been Peter's (I'm sure most people wouldn't want to be on the run from the king), but they were important enough for this angel to be sent to help him escape.

Perhaps it feels like God is delivering blow after blow in your life, or that he isn't on your side at all. But remember how we protect and guide our children here on earth – it isn't always good times and cuddles. There has to be discipline, tough choices and sometimes extreme action to protect those we love and help them to grow up to be the people we know they can be. God is exactly the same with us, and his plans are so much greater than anything we have planned for ourselves. So remind yourself that God *is* on your side and that he is working out something amazing through our lives.

Father God, help me to remember that you are on my side, however I feel about life right now. Please help me to grow into the person you want me to be and to accept your guidance, protection and discipline. Amen

RACHEL RIDLER

A hunger to know God

And the people of Berea were more open-minded than those in Thessalonica, and they listened eagerly to Paul's message. They searched the Scriptures day after day to see if Paul and Silas were teaching the truth. (NLT)

As a teenager, my parents would send me off every summer on Pathfinder camps to spend a week with other young Christians. At one camp, the older teenagers could come back as young leaders, and they gave them the name 'Bereans'. It always confused me, until later in life I finally got around to reading the book of Acts and came across this verse! The Bereans were a group of people who passionately wanted to find out the truth and learn more about God.

It seems fitting to me to end this series on Acts with the Bereans. Yes, there are many characteristics we can take from the early Christians – confidence, excitement, commitment to community, prayer, praise and a yearning to follow the Holy Spirit – but the Bereans' dedication to learning really stands out to me.

Maybe it's because I've been told so many times that 'leaders are learners' and encouraged to keep reading by those in ministry above me. Perhaps it's because I sometimes struggle to hear God's voice in the hubbub of our 24/7 world, but I know for sure that if I open up the Bible, I can hear from him there. Maybe it's because other people's doubts and arguments make it so easy to lose sight of why we believe what we do, and yet, whenever I come back to the Bible I learn, I hear, and I believe once again.

So may I encourage you today to take a page out of the Bereans' book and to become avid readers of the scriptures. Search for God in them every day and weigh up whatever you come across in your day-to-day life against the truth contained in those pages. This will give you the endurance to keep going in your journey with God and enable you to authentically share your faith with others.

Take some time today to open the Bible in a book that you are interested in and just read for enjoyment's sake. Be open to what God might say to you through his word today.

RACHEL RIDLER

Doorways, gates and portals

Chris Leonard writes:

'Bible notes on doors! Really?' My friend treated me to one of her looks. I too had been surprised to find such frequent mentions of doors and gates in the Bible. But then, haven't the scriptures served as a portal or doorway into the expanses of God's kingdom, often using objects that are familiar parts of everyday life, for millennia? Suddenly these ordinary things become doorframes through which we may enter further into God's heart.

Think about doors which hold special meanings, memories or associations for you – good or bad. Has a door been unexpectedly opened to you – or slammed in your face? You may be obeying Jesus' command to shut the door and pray in secret. Or taking a moment to realign with him, asking him to bless and be with you before rushing out for another busy day.

We may shut our doors, hurting others. Perhaps we even attempt to close God's doors in their faces. Closed doors, though necessary sometimes for defence or intimacy, often isolate or exclude. Is the door of your dwelling – of your heart and life – open to others or shut in fear, shame or defence?

Perhaps you are asking God to shut dark doors that lead into fear, lies or betrayal. Jesus described himself as the door, or gate, of the sheepfold, protecting the vulnerable flock at night from wolves and thieves. Perhaps you are praying he'll shield you from danger behind his sanctuary doors?

Shielding – ah! BRF arranged this topic with me long before Covid-19 and the March 2020 start of lockdowns had been imagined. That strange time continues as I write, so words like 'doors', 'shields', 'lockdown', 'going out' and 'coming in' have all gained unusual resonances.

With doors to church buildings shut by law, the church spilt out into the community and, my goodness, what new doorways have opened up there! In normal times, too, God will set before us open doors – varying our opportunities to work with and get to know him.

Our starting point has to be with Jesus, who has opened his sanctuary door for us to whisper our praises and prayers straight into the throne-room of the King of kings. As children of the King, we can address the Lord of all as our intimate friend, our daddy whose door is always open to us, his children.

Portals to...?

After this I looked, and there before me was a door standing open in heaven. And the voice… said, 'Come up here, and I will show you what must take place after this.' (NIV)

I wonder what you have found on the other side of the many doors through which you've passed in your life. Nothing as spectacular as John saw during his exile on Patmos, I suspect. Through a wide, open door, which appeared suddenly, John saw something completely 'other'. He saw another world – that of heaven itself, and I sense him struggling to find the words to describe it. How would you describe the majesty of a holy, eternal, triumphant, creator-God and Lord of all?

John had been flung behind the virtual prison doors of solitary exile on Patmos island simply for proclaiming Jesus. Having passed through doorways of suffering and patient endurance (1:9), he now stood on the threshold of another door. It led to extraordinary visions of things present and those to come.

Far beyond that small island at that point in time, John saw God's perspective on different churches, on earthly and heavenly powers, on evil, destiny and justice, on suffering and future glory. He saw the end of all our stories – the time when God's kingdom would come in all its fullness.

During the period of Covid lockdowns and social distancing, our sense of being in control collapsed. No one understood the disease, who would catch it next – nor how seriously. Most of our normal activities, economics, travel, roles, work and routines – even TV programmes and church services – stopped or changed as almost every area of the future became one big question mark. Would we ever see family members again to give and receive tangible support and love? Many Christians felt fear but, like John on Patmos, clung to God's eternal truths. Like John, we know the end of the story.

The verse 'All things hold together in Christ' (Colossians 1:17) became one doorway to hope for me when everything seemed to be falling apart. What were yours? You might try speaking them aloud as you praise him now.

CHRIS LEONARD

Narrow gate

'Enter through the narrow gate, because the wide gate and broad path is the way that leads to destruction – nearly everyone chooses that crowded road! The narrow gate and the difficult way leads to eternal life – so few even find it!' (TPT)

An art installation in the Austrian Alps reminded me of this passage. Several artists had each designed a door of the size normally found in a house. Hiking along some remote mountain path, we'd stumble across one. Unexpected and out of place, it opened like any normal door in its frame. Walking through it felt like entering a portal to another world – a fantasy tale come to life.

Why is Jesus' narrow gate hard to find? Is he saying we must search in remote places for this secret portal? (If his image refers, as many suggest, to a normal walled settlement with gates, surely people could have found the narrow path by leaving through a wide gate and walking round to it?) But the Greek word for 'gate' here can be translated 'mountain pass', which set me thinking of Tolkien's *The Lord of the Rings* and the difficult, narrow way the fellowship took over the mountains to evade enemies on the easier, valley route. Palestine had difficult, narrow passes among its rocky landscapes too.

Jesus goes on to say, 'Not everyone who says to me, "Lord, Lord," will enter the kingdom of heaven, but only the one who does the will of my Father who is in heaven' (v. 21, NIV). Jesus himself is the narrow gate. We find – and then enter into – his way through him. But he is no magic portal whisking us straight into heaven. In reality, most of us veer back towards our own way and struggle to follow the narrow path of doing nothing but the Father's will. No, we still have mountain passes to climb – hard work and painful sometimes – but he is with us, helping, growing and forming us all along the way.

Lord, you let us through the gate on to your path, accepting our flabby, dirty souls – then train us to run with you like athletes over 'impossible' mountains. You give your strength to help us become more like you. Thank you. Amen

CHRIS LEONARD

God's doors

Lift up your heads, you gates; lift them up, you ancient doors, that the King of glory may come in. Who is he, this King of glory? The Lord Almighty – he is the King of glory. (NIV)

I assume this psalm refers to the doors or gates of the temple – dreamt of, but not built by, the psalmist King David. He was inviting the one who founded and owns all of creation to come and live within those doors. According to 1 Kings 6, craftsmen carved on their special wood cherubim, palm trees and open flowers, hammering gold evenly over the top.

Panels of the gleaming bronze doors on Florence's Baptistery of St John (dubbed by Michelangelo 'The Gates of Paradise') display intricate bas-reliefs of biblical scenes. Strikes and upheavals when I was there forced those beautiful doors, along with those of all the art galleries in Florence, to remain shut, so we missed the treasures within. But God's glory fills earth and sky and has never been confined within the walls of church, temple or gallery!

Even doors that are precious works of art are nothing like as wondrous as those of God's temple of the Christian era. We are that temple, his special dwelling place. Our 'doors' are many, various and cannot be shut. We saw the truth of that during Covid lockdowns when more joined in church worship online or by video link than ever do in normal times.

In my church, trestle tables replaced chairs, as a large team first collected groceries and then prepared 200 food boxes each week to deliver to local families who would have been short of nutrition otherwise: God's people going out, loving, serving, helping others, having first entered the gates of his presence through praise and worship, albeit socially distanced. So let's 'enter his gates with thanksgiving and his courts with praise; give thanks to him and praise his name' (Psalm 100:4).

Why not look up Psalm 100 and sing it out in praise and worship (make up the tune as you go!). During lockdown I found that singing the psalms like this was a sure way into God's presence.

CHRIS LEONARD

Entering in

Open for me the gates of the righteous; I will enter and give thanks to the Lord. This is the gate of the Lord through which the righteous may enter. I will give you thanks, for you answered me; you have become my salvation. (NIV)

What a great psalm! 'He brought me into a spacious place' (v. 5), but how? Because the psalmist knew God, knew that his love endures forever and had just been praising him for it. Like the psalmist, I have felt hard-pressed recently. With hospitals full of Covid, I sat in a car park praying and singing psalms while my husband was diagnosed and then treated for a detached retina. Then it was my turn, with a melanoma.

The NHS was wonderful, but my anxiety brought huge pressure until I grasped that Jesus is himself our salvation. I am never going to get through the gate of the righteous by my own efforts, so he's given me his righteousness, his hope, his faith, his shalom-peace. He has himself, the one who was rejected and died, become my salvation. He has given me the key to his kingdom and invited me to enter in.

He gave Israel the promised land, too. When he told them to enter into and possess it at last, they listened to the wrong voices. They listened to the ten scouts, who said it would be far too much for them and lead to disaster, rather than to Joshua and Caleb who said (in Numbers 14), 'Go in God's strength.' The result? Israel remained in the wilderness for another generation.

Jesus has brought me into so many 'spacious places'. And yet, finding myself hard-pressed, often I'll reach the point of crying out to him in despair at my own weakness. Maybe it's only when I stop struggling and realise that I can't even trust him by my own efforts that his grace opens the door into the 'spacious place' that he has prepared for me – and gently eases me through it.

Lord, help us to enter into your salvation as our first, not our last, resort. Thank you for giving yourself to be our salvation, hope, peace and righteousness-enabler, and for the spacious place of your enduring love. Amen

CHRIS LEONARD

19

Locked doors?

Peter knocked at the outer entrance, and a servant named Rhoda came to answer the door. When she recognised Peter's voice, she was so overjoyed she ran back without opening it and exclaimed, 'Peter is at the door!' 'You're out of your mind,' they told her. (NIV)

A friend in her mid-80s was concerned about some elderly people living near her. When the pandemic restrictions were lifted and their 'shielding' ended, several refused to leave their home or even their bed. Having become conditioned to months of almost solitary confinement, they had become physically weak and too frightened to move. In effect, they had given up.

God sets the prisoners free and Peter found the courage to walk in that freedom, following the angel through the gates. His next problem was gaining entry to see the terrified friends who were still so earnestly interceding for his life. I love the fact that the little servant girl, who alone believed and was overjoyed, is named in this account. Good on her!

Next step was for God to release the others from their prison of fear. It took some convincing them that he could answer prayers miraculously. Strange, when some had seen the resurrected Jesus – seen how the might of Herod, Pilate, even death and the rock-sealed tomb were unable to hold him! But then I remember that Herod had James, John's brother, put to death shortly before Peter's imprisonment. I think my prayers too might well have been full of desperation rather than the faith to expect miracles.

I wonder if there are areas in which God has set you free but now you've stepped back, choosing confinement even though the 'door' is no longer locked. Like the disciples and those elderly people my friend knows, we too may feel weak, inadequate, helpless and shaky about walking with the Lord right out of danger and into the paths he sets before us. Peter, by contrast, having shared the good news with his friends, didn't hesitate to leave 'for another place', presumably at God's direction.

'It is for freedom that Christ has set us free. Stand firm, then, and do not let yourselves be burdened again by a yoke of slavery… The only thing that counts is faith expressing itself through love.' (Galatians 5:1, 6b)

CHRIS LEONARD

'Come in, come in'

When the disciples saw [people bringing babies to Jesus], they rebuked them. But Jesus called the children to him and said, 'Let the little children come to me, and do not hinder them, for the kingdom of God belongs to such as these.' (NIV)

One of my bright spots during lockdown was Malcolm Guite's YouTube site. He is a poet-priest-academic who retired as chaplain of Girton College, Cambridge in 2020. He spent that summer term in lockdown at home nearby. 'Come in, come in!' he would say, as the video played from the viewpoint of someone approaching the door of his study/library. 'Oh good, it's you! I've been wanting to show you this!' He'd produce some treasured volume and, as he talked about it, I'd think: 'Wow! How come I'm privileged to have this friendly and fascinating tutorial with a Cambridge don?' He has immense scholarship and loves the Lord too.

I'd studied English and Theology at another university, but, back then, I'd stand outside tutors' doors terrified. Most of them made me feel as if I knew nothing, whereas Malcolm Guite shares his heart as if with a friend. I know it's only on YouTube, but I feel like I have been welcomed into his home. I signed up to follow his channel and his blog, and have drawn much inspiration, comfort and wisdom from them.

Today's reading reveals much about how we welcome and treat others. The disciples had failed to understand that Jesus wanted their actions to reflect the way he welcomed and treated us. Though we're not on his intellectual, moral or spiritual level, Jesus throws open the door as we approach. 'Oh good, it's you! Come in, come in, there's something I want to show you.' And he gives us of his treasure – gems of his wisdom, generosity and love. Knowing him, we want to follow him, and to include others in that – anyone humble enough to sit at his feet and love him too.

My long-time favourite poem, and one of Malcolm Guite's, is 'Love iii' by the 17th-century poet-priest George Herbert. Do look it up online and then respond to it prayerfully. It starts, 'Love bade me welcome.'

CHRIS LEONARD

Shutting others out

'Woe to you, teachers of the law and Pharisees, you hypocrites!
You shut the door of the kingdom of heaven in people's faces. You
yourselves do not enter, nor will you let those enter who are trying to.'
(NIV)

These strong words of Jesus are repeated in Luke's gospel (11:52): 'Woe to
you experts in the law, because you have taken away the key to knowledge.
You yourselves have not entered, and you have hindered those who were
entering.' Easy for us to apply this to the Jewish religious leaders of history
– the gospels are full of stories about how they try to keep anyone poor or
disabled, those breaking obscure religious law and all women at a distance
from holy God. Nearer to our time, it's easy to see how church leaders kept
most of the population equally distant by offering worship and scripture
in a language few people knew – Latin – rather than in their native tongue.

Why are so many churches today segregated by colour? Because when
immigrants arrived with their vibrant faith, many 'white' churches failed to
make them welcome. Consider this: does your church or Christian organ-
isation shut the door against anyone? What people-groups does it fail to
make welcome or show the cold shoulder, even if not formally barring its
door to them?

Not one among us is worthy of being let into God's family, his house,
his body, his church. None of us gains admittance through our own merits,
so who are we to judge who will receive God's welcome, forgiveness and
redemption? Of course, if we let in some kinds of people we may well end
up with messy churches, but didn't Jesus come to heal the sick, redeem
the sinner, make the filthy clean and the unrighteous holy? Did he segre-
gate by race, status, gender or law-keeping? 'Do not judge, or you too will
be judged' (Matthew 7:1) could be rephrased: 'Do not shut the door on
others or you too will be shut out.'

---

*Lord, help us – and especially all in leadership – grasp that, in your kingdom,
only you are judge, only you are security guard. Amen*

CHRIS LEONARD

God seeks admittance!

'Here I am! I stand at the door and knock. If anyone hears my voice and opens the door, I will come in and eat with that person, and they with me.' (NIV)

How do you feel when knocking on someone's door? I expect it depends on your relationship with that person. Do you remember being summoned to the head-teacher's office having committed some misdemeanour at school? Have you knocked on the door of a prickly family member, irate boss or a doctor whom you suspect will bring bad news? Knocking on the door of good friends feels very different because you know you will be welcomed, feel at home and be able to be fully yourself.

That God bends to knock on our door seems an extraordinary thought. He's God – he could barge straight in and take control. But he doesn't work that way: he makes himself vulnerable to our ignoring his knocking. What kind of a God is that? The kind who came as a baby and died for us – the one and only God of love.

The Laodiceans appeared to have opened the door but not made him welcome, not accepted what he brought them. They kept him standing on their metaphorical doorstep, implying by their actions and attitudes that they didn't need him, nor place much value on his friendship or extravagant love.

I found this footnote in The Passion translation illuminating: 'In the days of Jesus, a bridegroom and his father would come to the door of the bride-to-be carrying the betrothal cup of wine and the bride-price. Standing outside, they would knock. If she fully opened the door, she was saying, "Yes, I will be your bride." Jesus and his Father, in the same way, are knocking on the doors of our hearts, inviting us to be the bride of Christ.'

Do I want Jesus as an occasional visitor or living in my house and involved in every aspect of my life, as a husband would be?

Lord, during the Covid lockdown, sometimes I overflowed with ingratitude, grumbling about seeing no one but my husband. I'd forget that you live in our home too!

CHRIS LEONARD

Knocking on God's door

'Ask, and the gift is yours. Seek, and you'll discover. Knock, and the door will be opened for you. For every persistent one will get what he asks for. Every persistent seeker will discover what he longs for. And everyone who knocks persistently will one day find an open door.' (TPT)

I have just written about how God loves to communicate – and to be – with us at all times but, in my experience, that doesn't always appear to be true. Some saintly followers of Jesus have described how God has appeared to hide for long periods, describing these as 'the dark night of the soul'. Several psalmists and other characters in the Bible concur.

Times like these test our faith. When we try to talk to him, it feels as if no one is there. It can seem illogical to believe that God exists or, at least, cares for us as he promised. Worship songs revelling in our intimate relationship and celebrating his constant presence become agony to sing. And yet, deep down, we know that God is true, we know that we have experienced his love and his grace, we know that his nature really is faithful commitment.

In this passage, Jesus is talking specifically about prayer. He's not saying: 'Ask anything in my name and it shall be done immediately,' nor is he explaining why it is that sometimes we have to seek and then knock persistently when God must have heard us the first time we asked.

I have prayed over decades for certain people and situations – yet nothing has shifted. I don't know why. I don't know why God appears to hide either. I suspect these are mysteries beyond our human understanding. Why would we be able to understand the plans of Almighty God fully? Perhaps he's encouraging us to exercise our 'faith and trust muscles' at such times. Maybe we grow stronger when faced with the resistance of 'shut doors'. Whatever his strategy, I'm very glad of Jesus' promise that we will one day find the door open again.

Lord, please send comfort and hope to any who feel you've deserted them at this time – and to those whose increasingly desperate prayers remain unanswered. Amen

CHRIS LEONARD

Doorway of hope – and opportunity

'I will give her back her vineyards, and will make the Valley of Achor a door of hope. There she will respond... as in the day she came up out of Egypt... You will call me "my husband"; you will no longer call me "my master".' (NIV)

'Achor' means trouble. I have found that God most often opens doorways of hope in my life when I'm going through troubled times, perhaps because I turn most readily to him then. After having one small, thin mole removed recently, I found myself entering a door marked 'Melanoma'. It provided unwelcome vistas into the strange 'country of cancer'.

Our wonderful NHS sent me to a long consultation with an eminent professor at a top London hospital. Then a session followed with a specialist nurse who became my second appointed keyworker. I staggered away with piles of literature and the promise of many more appointments, an operation and extensive scars. How does all this equate with my supposedly excellent prognosis? Whirling in a weird axis of hope, fear and confusion, I wondered: 'What's going on? And where are you, God, in all this?'

In researching these notes, I came across several references in the book of Acts to God 'opening doors' for the apostles to spread the gospel. In Colossians 4:3 Paul writes: 'Pray for us, too, that God may open a door for our message, so that we may proclaim the mystery of Christ, for whom I am in chains.' Paul never escaped that prison but, my goodness, through the letters he wrote there, his proclamations of Christ reached way beyond first century Colossae!

I'm no Paul. But could God want me as his ambassador in this particular corner of the 'country of cancer'? I am not relishing having more bits cut out of me, but many of my fellow patients will have many more reasons to fear. Instead of fretting, maybe I could pray that God will open doorways of opportunity for me to point someone I meet towards Jesus, who is himself the doorway to true hope.

Dear Lord, you open prison doors and extend your sure hope and warm hospitality to all who cry out to you. Help us to follow your example and see many doorways to your hope open in our 'valleys of trouble'. Amen

CHRIS LEONARD

Through your front door

These commandments… are to be on your hearts. Impress them on your children. Talk about them when you sit at home and when you walk along the road, when you lie down and when you get up… Write them on the door-frames of your houses and on your gates. (NIV)

I know lots of truths about God. But they are of little use unless they are worked out in my everyday life, attitudes, relationships and dealings with others. For example, I'm convinced that God is faithful, that he loves me and that I can leave all my worries with him. Do I live as though I believed these things? Very often, I don't. I know that God loves the unlovely and wants me to do the same. Do I act accordingly? Not often enough. I know he longs for me to be always open and listening to him, as he is to me. But, after ten minutes in the morning, sometimes I will happily ignore him for the rest of the day, as though it were mine!

Distractions, lies, worries, skewed focus, selfishness, sense of unworthiness – so many 'brakes' slow our spiritual progress. How can we break the unhelpful habits and thought patterns that can threaten to break our relationship with our faithful God?

Deuteronomy suggests one way. Each time Jewish people entered or left their homes they saw written reminders on the doorposts of how to work God's truths right into their lives. They may have been reminded too of the first Passover, when doorpost-blood saved their ancestors from the angel of death – or of a line in their 'hymn book': 'The Lord will watch over your coming and going both now and forevermore' (Psalm 121:8).

Here's another way. During the early stages of the Covid lockdown, each day a friend chose a different scripture that took 20 seconds to read – the minimum time prescribed for our frequent handwashing. She'd post it up in her downstairs cloakroom and recite it so often that not only did she learn it by heart, but she had also tuned her heartbeat more to God's.

Lord, show me practical ways to let your transforming truths suffuse my heart and life. Help me to pay attention to receiving your blessing as I go into and come out of my home. Amen

CHRIS LEONARD

Behind closed doors

Behind your doors and your doorposts you have put your pagan symbols. Forsaking me, you uncovered your bed, you climbed into it and opened it wide; you made a pact with those whose beds you love, and you looked with lust on their naked bodies. (NIV)

During lockdown, my church streamed its preaching series on the ten commandments. I joked with my husband that anyone wishing to commit adultery would have found very few opportunities in the previous months. But, behind closed doors, more children than ever were groomed for sexual abuse and calls to domestic violence helplines rocketed. Shocking numbers of violent crimes happen behind the closed doors of home. As Isaiah knew, these secret sins do huge damage.

I wonder if home is where I sin the most, if only because I spend most time there. Grumbling, complaining, criticising other people or speaking sharply to one's husband are not what Jesus tells us to do at home. Matthew 6:6 says, 'Go into your room, close the door and pray to your Father, who is unseen. Then your Father, who sees what is done in secret, will reward you.' That chimes with Isaiah's 'I live... with the one who is contrite and lowly in spirit, to revive the spirit of the lowly and to revive the heart of the contrite' (v. 15).

What else might we do behind closed doors that would please God? Make time to be creative, perhaps – to paint, write, cook? Or to contact lonely people by email, phone or video call?

When lockdown started, I worried about elderly folk living alone in my neighbourhood; but how to contact them? I felt a little nudge to do some digging in my front garden (on our property if not 'behind closed doors'). Everyone was allowed a brief walk each day, starting from home. Many walked down our road that morning, including all for whom I'd had concern – plus several I'd never met before. All welcomed the human contact as I asked if they needed help.

Pray for those suffering abuse, modern slavery or chronic loneliness behind closed doors.

CHRIS LEONARD

Guarding gates

Set a guard over my mouth, Lord; keep watch over the door of my lips. Do not let my heart be drawn to what is evil… He strengthens the bars of your gates and blesses your people within you. He grants peace to your borders. (NIV)

It is sad when some people feel the need to bar their windows or live in gated developments with cameras – and even armed guards. In Old Testament times, most people would have lived inside walled villages whose strong gates protected them against hostile tribes.

Psalm 147 promises not only strengthened gates, but also God's protection over their fields and crops, right up to the borders of their territory. There is so much in scripture about God being our refuge, our fortress and stronghold when we are in danger.

We can look forward to the heavenly city being without walls, without need for bars or gates, for there will be no evil; but what of the evil that still affects us now? For example, I know words that I have spoken or written have hurt others. Usually they have come tumbling out in thoughtless haste from my own unhealed pain.

Jesus said, 'Out of the abundance of the heart the mouth speaks' (Matthew 12:34, ESV). I think the old proverb should read, 'Sticks and stones may break our bones, but words can deeper harm us.' That's why the 'guarding prayer' in Psalm 141 is a good one to remember.

Yesterday I wrote about finding practical reminders to turn God-wards during our daily lives; today I have heard another example of someone doing exactly that. At the time of writing, we have to wear facemasks before entering shops and other crowded places. It feels negative and alienating. Revd Caroline Beckett wrote a special prayer for when masking-up for her Twitter account. It asks God to protect our lips from speaking anything harmful that day, as well as to protect ourselves and others from hurt and virus. You might like to pray my condensed adaptation of it below.

Lord, be my word-filter, whether or not I need to wear a physical mask today. May I breathe in the pure air of your love and then breathe it out on others as healing balm, and never as deathly virus. Amen

CHRIS LEONARD

Jesus himself is our gate!

'I am the gate; whoever enters through me will be saved. They will come in and go out and find pasture. The thief comes only to steal and kill and destroy; I have come that they may have life, and have it to the full.' (NIV)

A sheepfold had no gate apart from the narrow gap in its wall across which the shepherd would lie at night, protecting his flock from the thieves and wild animals who might attack them. Jesus, in describing himself as the sheepfold's gate, is promising to rescue us from clear and present dangers that beset us.

Saved from the jaws of the sea, from certain death, from those who would destroy or rob me, from an existence of crime, drugs, loneliness, rejection, disastrous decisions, misery – these are just some of the dangers that might cause an individual to call on Jesus, whose very name means 'Saviour'.

But there is so much more here. By laying down his own life, literally dying for us, Jesus has also unblocked the gateway that gives us access to the wide open 'pastures' of his Father. Jesus, the good shepherd, then leads us out into freedom, into possibilities previously undreamt of, into life in all its fullness where he will walk beside us, leading us to food and water, gathering us further into his flock.

Jesus is the gateway to life – life that is full and creative, overflowing with possibilities and with love, life that is joyful and eternal in quality. He is also our gateway into growth. We were created to be loving, good and true, and Jesus provides all we need to grow more like him and to point others towards him. We would never have been able to enter through that gateway had we trusted only in ourselves, in other people and our possessions. Jesus is the only way in!

Lord, be the defence at my family's and church's gate. Be my doorway out of any part of my life which imprisons – and my doorway into the fulness, the way, growth and freedom of your own life and kingdom. Amen

CHRIS LEONARD

Power to the sidekicks

Rachel Turner writes:

I have always been fascinated by the sidekicks in hero stories. The minor characters, who hover on the fringes of the unfolding story and pitch in to help the main hero achieve remarkable feats of bravery and rescue. Think of Robin, assistant to Batman; Bert, the plucky tag-a-long to Mary Poppins; and Lois Lane, lead journalist who Superman loves.

I have always felt a deep sense of injustice about the lack of credit given to these side characters. When you look at the stories closely, you will find that Batman would have died a thousand times without Robin's help. Bert was crucial in convincing Mary Poppins to do most of the fun adventures she did with the children. Lois Lane's fierce journalism discovered the felonious plots that Superman eventually waded into. Without these side characters, the main heroes would be a lot less super than they appear to be.

I think that sometimes women feel the pressure to be the superhero: The one who does it all, fixes it all, rescues it all. We can feel pressured to lead, to lift the weight off family or colleagues and be the hero others need. But maybe, just maybe, there is as much significance to how we choose to follow as there is in how we choose to lead. Perhaps there is strength in how we come alongside to be the minor character in someone else's hero story.

Scripture is full of minor characters, both powerful and subtle. Over the next two weeks, we will be delving into their contributions to the stories we know so well. We will look at how God empowered their choices and their contributions to impact those around them. We will be inspired to occasionally put aside our capes to be the best side character that can make all the difference in other people's stories.

Barnabas, the finder

Barnabas was a good man, full of the Holy Spirit and strong in faith. And many people were brought to the Lord. Then Barnabas went on to Tarsus to look for Saul. When he found him, he brought him back to Antioch. (NLT)

Barnabas was an effective leader in the early church, seeing many people coming to God as he preached and ministered in city after city. The disciples trusted him and gave him assignments that were vital to the growth of the early church. Barnabas appeared to be a hero.

Hero Barnabas was there to help when a new convert called Saul (later Paul) was struggling to be accepted by the church. Barnabas advocated for him before opposition resulted in Paul being sent back home for his own safety. Barnabas continued his growing ministry, in the thick of the expansion of Christianity, seeing lives changed and communities impacted.

Years later, fresh from ministry triumph, God prompted Barnabas about Paul. Barnabas chose to travel all the way to Paul's hometown to bring him back into ministry. Barnabas gave him opportunities to preach and lead, and became his partner in spreading the gospel. Barnabas chose to raise Paul up. Paul grew in impact and fame, and went on numerous missionary travels, eventually writing 13 books of our New Testament.

People across thousands of years have been encouraged through the ministry of Paul's writings such as, 'I can do all things through Christ who strengthens me,' 'My grace is sufficient for you' and 'There is no condemnation to those in Christ'. Barnabas appears today to be a minor character in the story of the early church compared to Paul.

My question is this: would we have had Paul without Barnabas?

There are people in our lives in desperate need of encouragement, of being found and lifted into their purpose. Generations to come may be blessed by who we choose to call out and pull alongside us. Who needs your voice of open welcome to step into what God has for them?

Almighty God, bring to our minds those who need our voice of encouragement and invitation. Give us a clear idea of how we can bring them alongside us and empower them, that we may see generations impacted by you. Amen
RACHEL TURNER

Huldah, the interruptible

So Hilkiah the priest, Ahikam, Acbor, Shaphan and Asaiah went to the New Quarter of Jerusalem to consult with the prophet Huldah. She was the wife of Shallum son of Tikvah, son of Harhas, the keeper of the Temple wardrobe. (NLT)

I can imagine the scenario. God's law had just been rediscovered, and, with horror, the king and the priests realised that they had been disobeying many commands for generations. They want to talk to God about the situation and so run to find someone who hears God clearly: a woman called Huldah.

We know very little about her besides where she lived, who she was related to and that it appears she was well known at the very highest levels as someone who hears God. I picture what it must have been like that day: Huldah getting on with her routine daily chores and then suddenly into her house bursts the king's priests, secretaries and attendants in a panic. She puts aside whatever is in her hands, listens to God and instructs them on what to say to the king. Then they all rush out again, and she picks up right where she left off.

I love how interruptible she was. I tend to be less so. When a phone call comes in, I pause and think, 'Do I have time to answer and deal with whatever it is, or shall I just let it go to a message and sort it out later?' I have my lists of things to do and places I need to go. I can make myself uninterruptible.

But sometimes the best ministry comes when we allow ourselves to be interrupted: to pause for a friend who needs to talk; to take that extra moment on the street to check on a stranger who looks distressed; to drop a text to an acquaintance at church who may need some scriptural encouragement. Huldah spoke God's words to a nation in the span of an otherwise ordinary day. What does God want to use us to do?

Father, help me to be interruptible for what you are doing. Please fill me with your peace that I may be ready to respond to those who need your words, truth and encouragement at the moment that they need it. Amen

RACHEL TURNER

Matthias, the replacement

'O Lord, you know every heart. Show us which of these men you
have chosen as an apostle to replace Judas in this ministry, for he
has deserted us and gone where he belongs.' Then they cast lots and
selected Matthias to become an apostle with the other eleven. (NLT)

Can you imagine having to be Matthias? Directly after they all watched
Jesus ascend to heaven, the first order of business became about who was
going to replace Judas as an official apostle. The disciples whittled the can-
didates down to two people. And then they cast lots, seemingly leaving it
up to chance, or God's guiding of the random roll. It came out for Matthias,
and he was welcomed into apostleship.

It doesn't feel like a comfortable role to be in: stepping into the spot left
vacant by Jesus' betrayer. Not necessarily a glowing mandate either. Jesus
handpicked all the other apostles, and here Matthias is being selected by
'you have been around for the right amount of time, let's see how God
works through this choosing process'. I wonder how Matthias felt about it.

Almost every role I've been in, there comes a point when I begin to
doubt myself. I start to think that someone else could do the job better
than me, or that I don't deserve the position I have been given. Matthias
teaches me that I'm right. None of the apostles were picked on their glorious résumés or merits. They were selected because Jesus chose them. He
shaped them, taught them, encouraged them and invited them into a role
that was more about Jesus than it was about them.

I don't have to be the best to be grateful that God chose me to do my
role. Sure, others may do it better, but he picked me. I can embrace the
utter joy and blessing of being chosen rather than judge myself to be
unqualified. I can trust the chooser. Matthias was chosen to be an apostle.
What a great honour. I am chosen too. And so are you.

---

*Lord, fill us with confidence that you chose us to fulfil the roles you have
called us into. We thank you for the invitation to adventure with you. Amen*
RACHEL TURNER

Naomi, the family maker

One day Ruth's mother-in-law Naomi said to her, 'My daughter, I must find a home for you, where you will be well provided for.' (NIV)

In this reading, we drop into the middle of a family story. Naomi is a grief-stricken mother, having lost her husband and children. Her daughter-in-law chose to stay with her, rather than go off and marry someone else. They formed this new little family, not linked by blood but by choice. Naomi loved Ruth as a daughter and worked on her behalf to help her find safety and a future. Eventually, the two women battle through poverty and living on the edges of society, and find a new home through Ruth's marriage to Boaz.

I see in this story such an expression of the heart of God for family. I love that this little family pulls together in the fire of grief, as these two women choose each other, not out of obligation but out of love and sadness. I'm reminded of the psalmist's words: 'God places the lonely in families' (Psalm 68:6, NLT).

Naomi had every excuse to go away and hide. She had lost her children and her husband. Her grief was all-encompassing. And yet, when her daughter-in-law wanted to stay with her, she found within herself the ability to love, sacrifice and work for Ruth's benefit. She chose to be family.

There are so many people around us who long for family and who need to be loved and to belong to someone: single people within our churches, widows, disenfranchised teens, young couples far from home and older generations disconnected from family. We have the ability to invite people into being loved like family and to work for their good as if they were family.

Naomi's commitment to Ruth led to her eventually marrying Boaz. Many generations later, Jesus is born, a direct descendent of this little family who found each other.

Father, shape us into your family. Guide us to those who need family and stir our hearts to love them as you love them, that many generations may be blessed through who you draw together today. Amen

RACHEL TURNER

Caleb, the faithful

'Today I am eighty-five years old. I am as strong now as I was when Moses sent me on that journey, and I can still travel and fight as well as I could then. So give me the hill country that the Lord promised me.' (NLT)

I think faithfulness is one of the most underrated qualities in life. It isn't a showy quality. Few people exclaim, 'Wow, did you see the faithfulness of that woman? Awesome!' Not many children declare, 'When I grow up, I want to be faithful.' Faithfulness isn't something that people notice straight away about a person, but it is a quality that is at the heart of who God is and what he values.

The word 'faithful' is used over 250 times in the Bible, describing God and what he looks for in his children. And so I want to pause to wave the flag for a person who exudes faithfulness: Caleb.

You may remember his name from an earlier story in the book of Joshua. God had led the Israelites to the edge of the promised land that he wanted to give them, and they sent in twelve spies to scope it out. The report was great, but most of the spies were terrified of the people already living in the land.

Only two spies stood against the fear and encouraged the Israelites to trust God and continue into the land. One was Joshua, who went on to take over from Moses leading the entire Israelite nation. And the other was a guy called Caleb, who went on to faithfully follow God, raise his family and, at the age of 85, fight to step into the land God promised him so long ago. A triumph of faithfulness.

I aspire to be as faithful as Caleb was: to unshakeably live my life with God's promises in front of my eyes; to weather the storms of work and family and health with a determination to cling to God through it all and serve others as he leads. God is so faithful to us. I want to be like him.

Father, give us the strength to walk each day faithful to you and your promises. Fill us with the grit and perseverance to find you in each circumstance, that we may live each day with you. Amen

RACHEL TURNER

Ananias, the brave

So Ananias went and found Saul. He laid his hands on him and said, 'Brother Saul, the Lord Jesus, who appeared to you on the road, has sent me so that you might regain your sight and be filled with the Holy Spirit.' (NLT)

In my Bible, this section is called 'Paul's Conversion', but I have always been impressed with the other individual in the story: Ananias. If I were writing the titles, I might rename this story as 'Ananias' Brush with Death' or 'Ananias Risks it All'. At this point, Saul (later Paul) was 'eager to kill the Lord's followers' and was travelling the country hunting them down. He had a fearsome reputation, and I'm sure the local Christians knew that Saul was headed their way. Out of nowhere, God appears in a vision to a local man called Ananias and gives him exact directions on how to get to Saul and what to do when he gets there.

I can't imagine the fear Ananias must have felt when he was told to go and pray for the hunter of Christians, the man who seeks the destruction of all who call on Jesus. To what dangers would Ananias be exposing himself and his family? There could genuinely have been a life-or-death situation by voluntarily showing up at Saul's location. But God believed so much in Ananias, that he didn't just tell Saul that *someone* would come and pray for him. Oh no. God told Saul Ananias' *name*. He was confident that Ananias would obey even in the face of fear. I would love to believe that God could ever be that confident in my bravery.

Occasionally I find myself relaxing into wanting to be used by God, as long as it doesn't cost too much. But the people who get to do great things with God are the ones who put obedience over safety, who say yes, no matter what it is. Ananias challenges me to put my whole life down and tell God I'm ready to be a part of his adventure.

Lord God, I am ready to say yes when you call, no matter what you put in front of me. Give me assignments that stretch me and scare me, that I may grow in boldness to say yes to you today. Amen

Eunice, the discipler

I remember your genuine faith, for you share the faith that first filled your grandmother Lois and your mother, Eunice. And I know that same faith continues strong in you. (NLT)

We read a lot about the role of one generation upon another in scripture. God commands each generation to share stories with the next, and to bring up our children to meet and know him. As Paul was writing to his younger friend, Timothy, he pauses to acknowledge that for Timothy, his mother and grandmother were significant in this generational passing on of the knowledge and love of God.

Every generation is significant in the lives of future generations. No matter what age you are, you are needed in the spiritual lives of those around you. If you are a parent or grandparent, you have been given significant influence in the spiritual lives of your children and grandchildren. In my work with Parenting for Faith, we have seen over and over again that it is never too late or too early to start influencing and encouraging the faith of your children, be they 60 years old or six months old.

If you are not a parent, there are children, teens and younger generations who need your influence just as much. Everyone needs someone older than them to tell stories of who God is and what he has done. Everyone needs someone older to believe in them, welcome them into friendship, and share life and laughter. Everyone needs someone more senior who will pray for them and love them.

If Paul the apostle recognises and praises the power of generations of faith-filled women upon the future leaders of the church, then we can be assured that our influence will shape the church now and in the years to come. Share your stories and where you see God in the world. You don't have to be perfect. Just be the authentic you, living your life with God and open to helping the next generation know him.

Father, give us favour in the eyes of those younger than us, that we may help them meet and know you. Remind us of the stories of what you have done in our lives, and who we need to share those stories with. Amen

RACHEL TURNER

Mordecai, the prodder

'Who knows if perhaps you were made queen for just such a time as this?' (NLT)

In the book of Esther, the hero of the story is the woman who risked her life, challenging the king to save the Jews from destruction. But would the Jews have been saved without her uncle Mordecai boldly prodding her to move beyond her fear and think of the needs of the nation? Would she have found the courage to act had someone not strongly encouraged her?

Eleven years ago, I was working in a church serving children and families. Sue Doggett, a commissioning editor from BRF, approached me and encouraged me to write a book to help parents learn how to bring up their children to meet and know God. I said that the idea scared me and I wasn't sure I was good enough. Sue turned up at a training day I was running, and firmly repeated the need for parents to have a book like this.

I told her I didn't know where to start. We met up for lunch and she presented me with a book proposal that she had written, based on the talks she had heard me share, and encouraged me to sign it. I did. Eleven years and seven books later, I work full-time with BRF serving parents and churches. I don't think I would be here without the prodding and encouragement of Sue Doggett.

There are people in our lives who need us to believe in them, to encourage them and to prod them to step into what God is calling them to do. Who do you see who is wrapped up in fear or hesitation? Who needs you to say, 'I see you! Jump in! God has great things for you to do! Who knows if perhaps you were put in your position for just such a time as this?' Never underestimate the power of being a Mordecai!

Father, give us eyes to see those who need some faith-filled prodding to step into what you have for them. Make us bold to encourage with strength, joy, and a love that can only come from you. Amen

RACHEL TURNER

Artaxerxes, the generous giver

And the king granted these requests, because the gracious hand of God was on me. (NLT)

Nehemiah is one of my favourite books in the Bible. I love the nitty-gritty soap opera of it all: the bravery, the backbiting, the paperwork exhaustion and the on-the-edge-of-your-seat readiness for battle. But I want to draw our attention to a minor character at the beginning of the story: Artaxerxes, king of the Persian Empire.

Nehemiah was moved to tears by the report of the state of Jerusalem and goes to his day job still affected by this emotion. He prays that God will give him favour with the king. Nehemiah's emotion so moves Artaxerxes that he agrees to Nehemiah's request. He gives Nehemiah a role in rebuilding, supplies letters of permission to political figures and even sends troops to protect him as he travels and carries out the job. An extraordinary display of generosity.

I am always baffled by his choice. I know there are many political reasons to agree to Nehemiah's request, but I'm always drawn back to a king seeing the sadness in a servant's face and taking the time to ask what is wrong. Nehemiah asked God for favour in the eyes of the king, and God responded by giving the king compassion. Out of that compassion, generosity flowed. I don't know whether Artaxerxes was typically this generous. I doubt it, and that challenges me. If this king, who did not know God, can be filled with his compassion and profound generosity, how much more can I?

How often do I set my heart for compassion? How often am I noticing the sadness of others and being prepared to respond with radical generosity? Artaxerxes was a part of God's fulfilment of his promises to his people. I want to be a part of that too.

Father, train my heart to see where generosity is needed. Soften my hand to be open to give what is required. Let me be a part of your provision for those you love. Amen

RACHEL TURNER

Saul, the empowerer

Then Saul dressed David in his own tunic. He put a coat of armour on
him and a bronze helmet on his head. David fastened on his sword over
the tunic and tried walking around, because he was not used to them.
(NIV)

We may have heard this story a thousand times: the epic tale of a child
conquering a giant with the power of faith and God. But I'd like to draw
your attention to King Saul in this story. In most of the stories we have
about King Saul, we would tend to put him in the 'flawed/possible villain'
category. He tries to kill David multiple times. He disobeys God; he hides
from taking the throne and then clings to it at the expense of everything.
But in this story, I think he does something brilliant.

When he hears that this teenager David is criticising him, he grants
David an audience to listen to what he has to say. He is so moved by David's
faith and connection with God that he decides to risk the entire battle on
him. People's lives are at stake, their future as slaves or freemen. Saul's
land and even his kingship may be at risk. And yet he didn't merely say,
'Oh, thanks, boy. Your words have really encouraged me. Oi! Soldier! Fight
with confidence! This boy says if we fight, God will be with us!' He instead
recognised that God was with this specific teenager and chose to raise him
up to fight for everything. I think that is a massively bold, faith-filled action
of leadership.

When Saul gave David his own tunic and armour, Saul was saying,
'You have my authority and my blessing.' I believe that we all have that
opportunity to raise up people around us and give them our authority and
blessing to do what God is calling them to do. Where do we need to give our
power to others so that we all might see what God wants to do?

---

*Lord God, show us where we can give our authority to others to enable your
plans to come to fruition. Let our hearts hear your voice through people of all
different ages and backgrounds, and enable us to empower all for your glory.*
RACHEL TURNER

Heman, God's musician

They and their families were all trained in making music before the Lord, and each of them – 288 in all – was an accomplished musician. (NLT)

I am writing this piece in the middle of one of the Covid-19 pandemic lockdowns. One of the things I deeply miss is corporate worship: the ability to gather together with other Christians and sing worship to God, side by side. I always feel so grateful to the worship leaders and musicians for facilitating our worship together.

At first glance, this passage is merely outlining the responsibilities of the worship leaders and musicians of the time. But a broader examination of the roles of these musicians is striking. They aren't tasked with playing music for a wide bunch of people. They aren't trained to lead corporate worship. The fundamental role of these musicians is to 'make music before the Lord'. Other verses describe their position as to 'minister before the Lord' with music. The musicians' job was to play directly to God; to bless, praise and love him through the medium of music.

These individuals and families with names I often cannot remember had an extraordinary job. They make me ask myself the question – when I worship in song, am I doing it for God or for me? Do I miss corporate worship because of what I receive out of it, or because of what I give to God in it?

This question has given my time at home a new lease of life. I am more aware of how bringing my amateur musician skills to a new song for God may be a sacrifice he loves. That my acapella singing to him as I cook may be a privilege of relationship that these biblical musicians may have envied. They had to physically be present in the house of the Lord to minister to God, while through Jesus Christ, I can have access to God anytime I want. What might your time with God look like?

Father, as we sing or play to you at home, come close to us. May your heart feel joy at our offering and may you know our humble, grateful love as we sing and play to you. Amen

RACHEL TURNER

Puah and Shiphrah, the ethical warriors

Then Pharaoh, the king of Egypt, gave this order to the Hebrew midwives, Shiphrah and Puah: 'When you help the Hebrew women as they give birth, watch as they deliver. If the baby is a boy, kill him; if it is a girl, let her live.' (NLT)

My first kickback against injustice was when I hid my broccoli in my milk to protest having to eat it. In a shocking display of magical knowledge, my mum noticed my innovative action and assured me that I could feel free to get down from the table when the milk had been drunk and the broccoli eaten.

Three hours and a lot of gagging later, I was freed. Eventually, I learned to distinguish between true injustice and things I just don't like, but that deep sense of wanting to fight what I viewed to be wrong was set in me. Because of that, Puah and Shiphrah have always been minor characters who I adore.

Puah and Shiphrah were women doing a tough job. Midwifery in biblical times must have been incredibly difficult, without working under a mandate from Pharaoh to murder children born with a specific gender. They brilliantly pivoted and managed to protect innumerable children. Scripture says that God was kind to the midwives and blessed them, approving of their fight for the lives of children.

What I find most encouraging is that in some ways their disobedience was not ultimately effective. Pharaoh continued to try to kill the boys, and policy continued. And yet God blessed the midwives. He included this story in the scriptures. He held these women up to us as leaders to admire, people who passionately protected life in the face of unjust commands and faithfully did what they could.

In our roles, be they paid or voluntary, we will be called upon to follow God's commands and to work for what is right. Regardless of the outcome, the effort to work with integrity on behalf of others pleases God and is a part of his master weaving of justice.

Father, show us where injustice is happening around us and let us play a small part in your plans. Bless the work of our hands, that we may walk with integrity the path of righteousness to which you call us. Amen

RACHEL TURNER

Jonathan's armour-bearer, the all-in friend

'Do what you think is best,' the armour bearer replied. 'I'm with you completely, whatever you decide.' (NLT)

There was a TED talk I saw entitled 'Leadership Lessons from a Dancing Guy', featuring a video from a music festival where a man was dancing on his own on the side of a hill. People were quietly laughing at him until one person leapt up, ran and joined him. Two people were now dancing exuberantly. Then a third and fourth jumped in. Within seconds, tens then hundreds of people ran to join this impromptu dance party, eventually lifting the original dancer upon their shoulders as he whooped and hollered with sheer joy.

Derek Sivers, the speaker of the seminar, highlighted that it wasn't the solo dancing guy who started this movement that ended up in hundreds of people dancing. It was the first follower – the bold one who first joined the lone dancing man. It was the second and third dancers who chose to jump in, so others felt compelled to follow. It was the followers who enabled the movement.

Jonathan's armour-bearer was a first follower. He told Jonathan that he was all in. His total commitment to join in enabled a mighty victory.

Leaders need first followers. They need clear-eyed Christians who will show up at their meetings, sign up for their fledging ministry efforts and loudly voice that we are all in because we believe in what they are doing. Never doubt that your presence and participation is essential. I cannot tell you the depth of encouragement that comes when someone steps out in faith and is met by a passionate first follower who says I'm all in. We are needed, my friends. Let's get dancing.

Father, give us the opportunities to be that significant first follower to those who need it. Take us on great adventures with those you bring us alongside, that we may see your ministry at work in our communities. Amen

RACHEL TURNER

Hur, the crutch

Moses' arms soon became so tired he could no longer hold them up. So Aaron and Hur found a stone for him to sit on. Then they stood on each side of Moses, holding up his hands. So his hands held steady until sunset. (NLT)

There are situations when people need someone to truly lean on – someone to hold them in place.

In this passage, Moses was overseeing a battle. God had placed Moses in this role, and when Moses' hands were up, the Israelites were winning the battle. But when he put his arms down, they began to lose. His companions couldn't do the role for him. They couldn't take his place. They could only help him do what he needed to do.

We rarely hear about Moses' companion, Hur. He is mentioned only a few times in scripture, primarily in this role as someone who assists Moses. He was vital to this battle. He wasn't just a support; he was the right support at the right time, which enabled victory for all.

When I had cancer, I needed support. I desperately wanted to continue to parent, to still do mum things, but I was exhausted. Several friends and neighbours came in to hold my arms: to drive my son and me to his club, so I could be there to smile at him without the exhaustion of driving; to do my laundry, so I had the energy to play with and listen to my son talk about his day after school. They held me in place so I could do what only I could do, be my kid's mum. I am forever grateful.

It may seem like a little thing, like anyone could do these mundane support tasks. But not many people are willing to sacrifice and love in such a way. It is displaying the servant heart of Jesus, to love so that others may flourish. May we all be like Hur for each other.

Father, give us eyes to see who needs a Hur in their life. Fill us with your love that we may hold other's arms up. And if we need those Hurs in our lives now, please send them to us that we may be held, too. Amen

RACHEL TURNER

God's love song
(Song of Songs)

Lyndall Bywater writes:

Friends of ours wanted a reading from Song of Songs at their wedding, but there was a twist. You see, they wanted a dramatic reading. They didn't want someone delivering it in a typical church-Bible-reading monotone; they wanted it read like it was meant to be read, as two people having a tender, passionate conversation with each other.

They asked couple after couple, but they all said no. Clearly it was just a bit too exposing to declare, before a church full of people, that your beloved has breasts like young deer! In the end, my husband and I were the only couple they could find who were willing to give it a go.

Song of Songs isn't an easy book to read, even when you're not declaiming it aloud for a wedding congregation. The imagery is obscure to us, perhaps because compliments tend to be born out of the context in which we live. For instance, our modern western culture is heavily influenced by wealth, so it's not surprising that we describe beautiful eyes as shining like diamonds, hair as being like spun gold or skin as being as smooth as silk. If you had lived in an agrarian economy, where cattle were your greatest wealth, you might well be more inclined to call on the beauties of sheep and goats for your compliments.

What's more, the structure is complex. It's a collection of mini-poems, if you like, some in the voice of the man (in these notes I'll call him 'the Lover'), and some in the voice of the woman (whom I'll call 'the Beloved'). Still others are in the voice of a group looking on, a bit like a chorus.

To make it more confusing, there are discrepancies in the different translations about who said what, so don't be surprised if you have words in your translation which I seem to have attributed to the wrong person.

All that being said, this is, in my opinion, one of the most beautiful and astonishing books in the Bible. I discovered it relatively young and have loved it ever since. Even to grasp the tiniest part of what it says about God's love for us is life-changing. To receive those words of love at the deepest place within yourself is profoundly healing.

As you read, just remember, having teeth like sheep is apparently a good thing!

Longing love

Kiss me and kiss me again, for your love is sweeter than wine. (NLT)

Does anyone else feel as uncomfortable as I do about a woman starting a conversation with the words 'kiss me'? It feels so forward and so brazen somehow, doesn't it? Surely a more appropriate opener would have been something more reserved like: 'Can I make you a coffee?'

There is absolutely nothing reserved about Song of Songs. It's a book full of vibrant emotions and raw passion, and it is, in part, about a woman who isn't afraid to speak the truth about herself and how she feels.

The first thing she tells us about herself is that she doesn't think she's beautiful. Perhaps women down the ages haven't changed that much, after all. She calls herself 'dark' because of her sun-browned skin, a characteristic that wasn't prized in ancient cultures as much as it is in ours, and she owns up to having irritated her nearest and dearest from time to time. But she also knows that she's done much for others, tending their vineyards at the expense of tending her own.

It's been a mixed bag of a life so far, but she's learnt to value what matters most and to go after it, no matter how 'forward' that makes her. This love she's found is better than wine and oil, two of the most precious substances in the ancient world. This love is something she doesn't want to keep at arm's length. She wants this love all over her, around her, inside her… and she's not afraid to say so.

We women can be desperate for so many things: desperate to look right, desperate to be on good terms with everyone, desperate to help others, often at the expense of ourselves, but do we let ourselves express that deep inner desperation to be kissed by love?

What are you most desperate for? How has the answer to that question changed over the years?

LYNDALL BYWATER

Defining love

Behold, you are beautiful, my love; behold, you are beautiful; your eyes are doves. (ESV)

Think of someone you've known for years; someone you love and with whom you've had a strong relationship. What did you like about them when you first knew them? And what do you like about them now? I'm going to guess that the second list is longer than the first, because it's as we get to know people that we discover the very best things about them. We may discover their dark side, but we also see more and more of their beauty.

Right at the heart of the love relationship in Song of Songs is the mutual appreciation of beauty. The Lover thinks the Beloved is beautiful and she thinks he is beautiful, and they don't stint on telling each other so. Yet all too often we don't believe we're beautiful and we don't see how anyone else could think that about us, especially God, who sees the deepest, darkest parts of ourselves.

You and I are made in the image of God. God is beautiful; therefore we are beautiful too. We may have been scarred and tarnished along the way, living in a broken, fallen world, but we are beautiful. The God who made us and knows us isn't deluded about our darkness, but neither is he blinded by it. He sees beyond our flaws to the beauty of all that we are, all that we've become and all that we will be.

Did the Beloved in Song of Songs struggle to believe she was beautiful? Is that why her Lover repeats the phrase several times in quick succession? God longs for us to know that we are beautiful, and he will never stop telling us. It can be hard to hear him saying it, and even harder to receive it, but it is absolutely and unchangingly true.

Lord, you call me beautiful. Where my own flaws or the opinions of others have planted in me the lie that I'm not, I ask you to uproot it. Set me free to know I am yours, beautiful and beloved. Amen

LYNDALL BYWATER

Immersive love

His left hand is under my head, and his right hand embraces me! (ESV)

During the summer of 2020, somewhere between the first and second lockdowns of the year, I attended a theatre production in London. It was described as 'immersive', and they weren't wrong! We all sat in the pitch dark wearing headphones, while special sound technology made us feel as though a rather unhinged woman was hugging us and whispering in our ears. It was brilliant but extremely intense.

Immersive is a pretty good word to describe the love which the Beloved receives in Song of Songs, though I'm assuming she was less disturbed than I was at the theatre. If you look carefully at today's verses, you'll find that her Lover quite literally wraps around her in his love. He is the shade and the banner above her head; he has his arm around her, and his hand cradles her head. As if that weren't enough, his love fills her with nourishing, sweet goodness.

I don't know about you, but I've lived a lot of my life knowing that God loves me in theory, but not really knowing what that feels like in practice. I find this little poem picture helps me connect more deeply with the experience of God's love for me. He is the apple tree that shields and shades me with protection. He feeds me when I feel weak and drained. He cherishes me in his strong embrace. He even holds my head up when everything gets too much. And, perhaps most amazingly of all, he celebrates me by waving his banner of love over my head.

And what does the Beloved do while all this loving is going on? She's at rest, sitting under a tree, enjoying a banquet and resting in his arms. Might we experience more of that immersive love if we stopped to rest?

Which aspect of God's love do you most need to experience today: the protection of the apple tree, the joy of the banquet or the tenderness of the embrace? Don't be afraid to ask, and don't forget to rest.

LYNDALL BYWATER

The voice of love

Listen! I hear my lover's voice. I know it's him coming to me – leaping with joy over mountains, skipping in love over the hills that separate us. (TPT)

The voice is a powerful thing. It's one of the first things babies learn to recognise, along with faces, partly because the brain processes sound more quickly than light. What we hear gets into our heads more quickly than what we see. In fact, vocal recognition sinks so deep in us that we can pick out a familiar voice from amidst a veritable cacophony of noise. Voices connect us with one another, even when we can't see each other.

After the immersive intimacy of yesterday's Song of Songs passage, we arrive at verse 8 to find that the Lover has gone away for a time. The Beloved is missing him, of course, but then she hears his voice, and her joy is restored. When life feels lonely, a much-loved voice can bring comfort and warmth. When it feels as though God is distant, a word from him can set our hearts at peace. But the appreciation goes both ways. In verse 14, we learn that the Lover loves his Beloved's voice too. He tells her that her face is beautiful, but so is her voice.

There are all kinds of excellent reasons to pray – to take time out of our busy lives to talk with God – but one of the most important reasons is simply that he loves to hear your voice and he loves to teach you to recognise his, so you will always be able to pick it out from amidst the cacophony of life.

There are more voices in this passage, though. There are voices singing to herald the spring and the cooing of turtledoves, birds which tend to sing at harvest time. One of God's most beautiful demonstrations of love towards us is to gift us a world brimming with beautiful voices and beautiful song.

If you can, find time today to listen to the sounds of nature, whether by going outside or listening to a recording. Sink into the sounds, listening as though it's God's very own love-song to you.

LYNDALL BYWATER

Proud love

King Solomon built his own royal carriage from the trees of Lebanon. He had its posts fashioned from silver, its back made of gold, its seat covered with royal purple, its interior decorated with love by the young women of Jerusalem. (VOICE)

'You've got to have a special car,' said my mum at least 20 times in the run-up to our wedding. We really weren't that fussed, but since she kindly offered to foot the bill, we duly booked the 1920s Bentley. If you have ever travelled in such a vehicle, you'll know they're not made for voluminous wedding dresses and trains, but as we made our stately way through the city after the wedding ceremony, I found myself rather glad to be marking that special day in such splendid style.

Our racing-green Bentley had nothing on Solomon's wedding car though! In Hebrew tradition it was the groom who arrived in style, rather than the bride. If money were no object, he would fashion a carriage fit for the bride he had been waiting, working and longing for throughout the betrothal, and then, once the vows had been exchanged, he would welcome her to sit in it with him and they would parade through the streets. The carriage would have been a statement of his wealth, but, more than that, it would have been a statement of his pride in the one he was marrying.

Do you ever stop to think about God being proud of you? You can become so caught up in your own shortcomings, thinking about all the ways you could be and do better, that it's easy to lose sight of the truth that your loving God delights in you. You bring him joy just by being yourself, and he loves to show you off to the world. Like the Lover in Song of Songs, he is ecstatic that you have chosen to join your life to his, and he welcomes you to sit close beside him, riding through life in splendid style.

Ask God to tell you about the carriage he'd make for you if he were going to show you off to the world. Let the Spirit paint a picture of it in your imagination. You could even draw it.

LYNDALL BYWATER

Captivated love

You are altogether beautiful, my love; there is no flaw in you. (ESV)

Compliments have obviously changed somewhat over the centuries, haven't they? We've reached the wedding night in this story of courtship and consummation, and while it's clear that the Lover is utterly delighted by his new bride, his compliments just don't seem very romantic to me.

When I think about a flock of goats leaping down a mountain, I just think 'smelly and wild', which isn't something I'd ever want said about my hair! Cheeks like pomegranates… is that a comment on my spots? It's all the hormones, I tell you! And don't get me started on breasts like baby deer… I suppose they were pert and bouncy once; nowadays they're more like droopy old nags.

Even if we can make sense of the compliments, this intensely physical passage can be an uncomfortable read. Christianity has often shied away from talking about physical beauty or sexual attraction for fear of encouraging inappropriate or immoral behaviour, and passages like this have often been interpreted in a purely spiritual way. What's more, many of us have a strong disgust response to our own bodies. When we look at ourselves, we don't see beauty; we just see all the things we think make us ugly. But if we skim these passages or over-spiritualise them, we miss something really precious.

The one who knit you together, who knows you, who chose you and who delights in you, calls you flawlessly beautiful. It's not just a 'spiritual' love; he loves every inch of you, right down to your cellulite and your droopy boobs. That's your starting point. You may wish to change things about yourself, and he will help you do that if it's a healthy choice, but know that there's nothing you can do to make yourself – soul, mind or body – more beautiful to him.

Which mirror do you look in most often? Find a lipstick or felt-tip pen and write the words 'flawlessly beautiful' on it. Whenever you look at yourself, you'll be reminded of how God sees you.

LYNDALL BYWATER

Welcoming love

You are a garden locked up, my sister, my bride; you are a spring enclosed, a sealed fountain … You are a garden fountain, a well of flowing water streaming down from Lebanon. (NIV)

The people we love most are the least boring to be with. You may disagree if you're regularly treated to steam-train lectures, of course! The reason companionship and the joy of togetherness grow over the years is because there is always more to know about each other, and there's nothing more wonderful than discovering things about each other you never knew before. Perhaps when we get bored of each other it's because we've stopped wanting to discover more.

Today's passage is the second part of the wedding night poem, and it's an attempt to put into words the joy the Lover has in discovering things about his Beloved which he didn't know – couldn't have known – before they married. She welcomes him into herself and he is intoxicated. It can be a difficult passage to apply to our own relationship with God, because surely he knows everything there is to know about us, doesn't he? He's been with us every moment of our lives and he knows us completely already.

The main image in this passage is of unlocking. The Beloved is a garden and a spring of water, enclosed within her own boundaries, and she has a choice about opening herself up to her Lover. This is no 'break and enter'; it's a willing welcome, inviting him into the places she has never opened to him before.

God may know everything about you, but he still longs to be invited into those secret, hidden places of your life you've been keeping locked up. You may fear what he'll find there, but he knows there are rich, precious things in you. You may think he just wants access so he can clean you up, but apparently he longs to enter because he knows there are wonders to discover in you.

Ever-loving God, help me to open up those places within myself which I tend to keep locked away when I'm talking to you. I know you'll treat my tender places with honour, so I open the door and welcome you in. Amen
LYNDALL BYWATER

Absent love

I opened for my beloved, but my beloved had left; he was gone.
My heart sank at his departure. I looked for him but did not find him.
I called him but he did not answer. (NIV)

When I was young, my Christian faith was nurtured in the incubators of Christian conferences and summer camps. They really were mountain-top experiences. God felt so close at those times, and I'd head home thinking I'd finally cracked it. Never again would I doubt his love or wonder if he even existed. Fast-forward 48 hours and you can probably imagine what had happened. I was back in the doldrums of discouragement, with a healthy dose of shame on the side for obviously being such a flaky Christian.

After the heady glories of the wedding night, chapter 5 of Song of Songs comes as something of a shock. What on earth has happened? The Lover comes to his bride; she takes a while to get herself out of bed and by the time she opens the door, he's gone. She then goes looking for him, only to get beaten and sexually assaulted by those who are meant to be protecting her. It's catastrophic, but I'm deeply glad it's here in the story, because it's what far too many of us have lived through: the exhilaration of experiencing God's love turning into a nightmare of loss, sorrow and pain, for no apparent reason.

All the emotions of those seasons are here: guilt that she didn't show her love by getting up more quickly; fear that she's broken their relationship irrevocably; devastation at being abused by those in leadership and misunderstood by her friends. It's all here because it's all real and it can happen to any of us. Before you rush ahead to find resolution, take heart today in the truth that sometimes bad things just happen. It doesn't mean it's your fault, it doesn't mean God has abandoned you and it certainly isn't the end of the story.

If anything in the passage or anything I've written today resonates with you, please make time to speak to someone you trust. Don't let guilt or shame make you feel like you have to walk through this dark place alone.

LYNDALL BYWATER

Loyal love

His mouth is sweetness itself; he is altogether lovely. This is my beloved, this is my friend, daughters of Jerusalem. (NIV)

What's the most annoying thing anyone can say to you when you've lost something? Let's all repeat it together, shall we: 'Where was the last place you had it?' If you are anything like me, you follow that supremely unhelpful question with a muttered: 'If I knew that, I wouldn't have lost it, would I?'

However annoying the question may be, the principle of retracing your steps to recover what you've lost is a good one, and it's what the Beloved does here in the second part of chapter 5. She goes back to what she knows. She remembers what her Lover was like the last time she felt close to him. In fact, she waxes lyrical about him.

So far, the most eloquent poems in the book have been his descriptions of her, but now it's her turn to extol his beauty, right in the middle of her deepest crisis. She recalls the intimate details of his body, but the physical characteristics tell a deeper story. She remembers him as strong, solid, gentle, pure and sweet. That's what he was like when she last felt him close, and that's who he still is, even if he seems a million miles away.

Perhaps you've tried to praise God through the pain, but it's just felt like an empty exercise in positive thinking, or yet another way to beat yourself up. That's not what the Beloved is doing here. She is remembering. What do you remember about God in the deepest part of yourself? What aspects of his character have you experienced most powerfully over the years? You may have been hurt by Christians; your experience of church may have been unhelpful at times; but God is unchangingly good, and if you've ever tasted that goodness, it is well worth remembering.

Valentine's Day is the day for flowery poetry. Why not pen a poem listing all the good things about God you've ever tasted? He may feel far away, but he is altogether lovely and he is your friend.

LYNDALL BYWATER

Secure love

My beloved has gone down to his garden, to the beds of spices, to browse in the gardens and to gather lilies. I am my beloved's and my beloved is mine. (NIV)

Staying connected with your loved one while you're apart is probably one of the most precious arts of building a lasting relationship. Before technology came along to aid us in our communications, letter-writing was the only option. I always used to marvel at how lovers would write to each other every day, even if the letters would be two weeks out of date by the time they arrived.

Nowadays the average mobile phone has at least six ways of reaching your nearest and dearest at the touch of a button. But of course what matters most isn't so much the means of connecting as the desire to be connected.

Things have moved on again in our lovers' tale. The intensity of consummation has passed, as has the bleakness of trauma and separation. Chapter 6 finds the couple getting on with day-to-day life, warmed by their love for each other. It seems the Lover might have been travelling, since he's taken to comparing his Beloved's beauty to that of the finest cities he's ever seen.

For her part, the Beloved is getting on with some farming, checking how the crops are doing… and perhaps turning her thoughts to the budding of new life in other ways too.

But woven through it all is a tender connectedness. He uses the same words to describe her as he used on their wedding night. This time, when she's asked where he is, she's not bereft but at peace. She sums up their contentment beautifully: whether together or apart, she is his and he is hers.

If two humans can be that contentedly connected, how much more can we enjoy that same connectedness with God, who needs no phone network or postal system to speak his words of love into our souls?

One of the best ways to carry God's words of love with you throughout the day is to learn Scripture off by heart. Why not learn the verse at the top of today's note, then repeat it throughout the day?

LYNDALL BYWATER

Reassuring love

The feelings I get when I see the high mountain ranges – stirrings of desire, longings for the heights – remind me of you, and I'm spoiled for anyone else! Your beauty, within and without, is absolute, dear lover, close companion. (MSG)

It's a well-known fact that complimenting a woman on her appearance when she's feeling out of sorts can be a dangerous business. The wise know that the answer to the question 'Do I look fat in this?' is always 'No', and the answer to the question 'How do I look?' is never, ever just 'You look fine'! The wise have also taken time to learn how to walk the tightrope between truthfulness and flattery, and if that has proven too difficult, they've honed the simple art of making her laugh.

I can't help wondering whether this fulsome rhapsody on the Beloved's physique was the Lover's response to her feeling distinctly cranky and down on herself. It's a thorough-going appreciation of her whole body, from her toes to her nose. Perhaps she'd just been on one of those self-loathing rants we sometimes go on:

'My feet are swollen and hideous. Look at my thunder thighs! I'm so fat. My boobs are saggy… and don't get me started on how ugly my face is!' You may smile in recognition as you read those words, but hating your body is a dark place to be, isn't it? For many of us, it's a low-level frustration, but for some it can lead to self-harm, eating disorders and a host of other mental health struggles.

Perhaps the 'toes to nose' appreciation was to encourage the Beloved or make her smile, but it was a wise strategy for boosting her mental health too. It's so easy to obsess about one particular feature of our bodies. Yet the truth is you're not just a stomach or a pair of thighs. You are a whole person, a beautiful work of art, made up of many parts, and you're desirable inside and out.

Lord God, you designed me and you created me. Please forgive me for hating myself. Teach me to love myself: body, soul, mind and spirit, so that I can enjoy and revel in the truth that you love me completely. Amen

LYNDALL BYWATER

Self-giving love

The mandrakes send out their fragrance, and at our door is every delicacy, both new and old, that I have stored up for you, my beloved. (NIV)

From our 21st-century vantage point, it's hard to imagine what a royal marriage would have been like in ancient Near Eastern culture one thousand years before Christ. In that time, a king like Solomon would have had hundreds of wives and concubines 'on demand', so to speak, women who would have had no rights to refuse him without fear of losing their means of survival. The power dynamic was brutal in its inequality.

Given that culture, Song of Songs is a surprising story, attributed as it is to King Solomon. It's the tale of a relationship which seems to have both equality and reciprocity, and that comes into focus in today's passage. Instead of the Beloved being swept up and whisked off by her more powerful Lover, it's her turn to lead him somewhere; to open something to him which he can't have unless she gives it; to give him treasures which even he, in all his wealth, doesn't possess.

We might not face significant inequalities in our human relationships, but when we think about being in relationship with God, the inequalities are obvious. God is all-powerful and all-knowing. The riches of creation are his. He made us and he sustains us. Everything we are belongs to him; everything we have comes from him. Yet this passage seems to suggest we have treasures ('delicacies') we can give him. That is an astonishing thought!

The substance of God's relationship with creation is love. That's the only way he ever relates to anything, including us. Love never forces itself or takes what isn't offered. It waits to be invited and then it revels in the joy of being welcomed.

There are treasures in you which you can choose to give to God. If you do, it will thrill his heart.

Take time today to ask God what treasure he sees in you. What are the things which bring him delight? What treasures, 'new and old', do you see in yourself? What would it mean to give them to him today?

LYNDALL BYWATER

57

Passionate love

Set me as a seal upon your heart, as a seal upon your arm, for love is strong as death, jealousy is fierce as the grave. Its flashes are flashes of fire, the very flame of the Lord. (ESV)

Have you ever noticed that intensely passionate love is only really safe and healthy when it's reciprocal? When one person loves another but that love isn't returned, the result can be a dangerous, destructive obsession or an unrequited longing that wounds the soul deeply. Perhaps that's why we hope and pray that love will fade if the person we long for doesn't return our love.

The final verses of today's passage are some of the most famous in the whole book. They are often read at weddings and funerals, and they are beautiful indeed, but they are also wild. They talk about this intense love which can consume and destroy if it's not handled properly. This kind of love is as strong as death. It's tenacious and unyielding in its jealousy. It burns like a consuming wildfire that can't be put out, even with a river of water.

Yet it is also described as being like 'the very flame of the Lord'. If you ever thought God's love was cosy and tame, you've probably begun to think otherwise in the past two weeks, but here's the proof that it's anything but. The love God longs to share with you is something breath-taking and exhilarating, and it's meant to be fully reciprocal. We're invited to love God with the same fiery love he feels for us.

If you've been burned by love in the worst sense of the word, through rejection, abandonment or infidelity, it may feel like an unsafe business, welcoming such intense feelings into your heart; but the one who invites you on this wildest of adventures loves you absolutely and completely, and he will never let you down. No matter how intense your love, desire and longing for him, his love, desire and longing for you will always be stronger.

As you've read Song of Songs, have you noticed any reticence or fear in your heart at the thought of such an intense love relationship with God? Ask God to show you where that fear or reticence comes from.

LYNDALL BYWATER

Completing love

But now I have grown and become a bride, and my love for him has made me a tower of passion and contentment for my beloved. I am now a firm wall of protection for others, guarding them from harm. (TPT)

I first read Song of Songs when I was going through a tough time at university. I couldn't make any sense of most of it, since the Hollywood romance culture I'd imbibed as a teenager never referred to any part of a woman as being like goats or sheep or fawns, but I somehow connected deeply with the idea of that passionate love relationship with God. I somehow knew that if I could find it, it would put a fire at the core of my being that would heal me and help me love others.

This final passage of the book shows just how far our heroine has come on her journey of love. She is content: content with her body (proudly describing her own breasts as towers) and content with the treasures of her own vineyard, which she knows is hers to offer, and which she knows her Lover will never tire of. She's begun to give more advice to the younger women around her, no longer just sticking to the rather mysterious and tantalising 'don't look for love before it finds you' mantra. It's as though the flame of love she shares with her Lover has ignited a fire of compassion, courage and confidence in her which radiates warmth to the world around her.

Does she ever grow out of that consuming passion which has carried her through the uplands of intoxicating joy and the crevasses of grief? It would seem not. The final poem ends with her calling to her Lover in the same language she used at the start. He is still her young stag, and their mountain is still bursting with spice.

No matter how mature and responsible we become, we need never lose that fiery passion that draws us ever deeper into God.

Lord, save me from becoming so burdened by life that my relationship with you becomes mechanical. May the fire of love in my heart grow ever stronger, burning with passion for you and compassion for your world. Amen

LYNDALL BYWATER

The prayer of confession

Helen Williams writes:

'Chocolate seashells, so small, so plain, so innocent,' confesses one character, 'I thought, "Oh, just one little taste."' 'And it melts,' admits another. 'God forgive me, it melts ever so slowly on your tongue and tortures you with pleasure.' The young priest in the film *Chocolat* is inundated with such confessions after a woman arrives in the tranquil French village, sets up an alluring 'chocolaterie' (during the season of Lent) and upsets the strict order of life!

Ash Wednesday next week marks the beginning of Lent for us. I wonder how you approach this season – traditionally a time of penitence and reflection before the joy of Easter. Whether you are used to observing Lent or not, whether or not you will be giving up chocolate, I invite you to join me in thinking about what confession means and asking God for his wisdom. We will be doing this through the lens of two of David's penitential psalms – Psalm 32 and 51.

The Bible contains around 1,500 references to words meaning 'sin'. As a society, we may have a fairly strong moral sense in terms of human rights, mutual tolerance, environmental awareness and caring for the vulnerable; but talk of 'sin' often makes people, even us, uneasy. It can conjure up something puritanical and life-denying.

As Christians, we know that God calls us to a life of holiness, not sin, but it can be daunting. Timothy Radcliffe is encouraging in his book *Alive in God* (Bloomsbury, 2019): 'This perfection cannot be arrived at through grim determination and self-flagellation. It is a gift that unfolds as one lingers in his company, dwells on his word and shares his life.'

Jesus' first recorded words, on coming out of the desert (the period we now echo in Lent), are: 'The kingdom of God has come near. Repent and believe the good news!' (Mark 1:15, NIV). The need to be rid of sin was central to Jesus' message, and he goes on to teach us how in the Lord's Prayer: 'Forgive us our sins as we forgive those who sin against us' (and in his parables), but then he actually becomes the Way for us to be saved, through his death.

Reading both psalms before starting this week's notes might be good, as we will inevitably be jumping around a bit from day to day. As we begin, let's linger in his company, dwell on his word and accept his gift.

Clouds and consequences

When I kept silent, my bones wasted away through my groaning all day long. For day and night your hand was heavy on me; my strength was sapped as in the heat of summer. (NIV)

I have just returned from an amazing trip to see my daughter in Kenya. If you have been privileged to fly, you'll know it's not unusual to take off from a UK runway, as I did, and find yourself climbing swiftly through banks of thick, grey cloud. As the aircraft climbs, however, it pushes through this barrier and out into an astonishing world of bright sun and vistas of white fluffiness.

As I gazed out of the plane's window, I was reminded of a simple diagram I grew up with – a stick person (me), and above me a large cloud (sin), and above the cloud the word 'GOD'. There have been many times in my life when this picture has been really helpful. You'll know those seasons when you feel dry, dissatisfied and disconnected from God, while knowing that it's not him who's absented himself. Usually we just need to ask the Holy Spirit to highlight what's out of kilter in our life, where we've gone wrong and what we might need to confess.

I've always loved Psalm 32 – it's very personal but also extremely practical. This is what happens, says David, when I try and hide my sin away from God: 'I end up groaning all day long; my very skeleton disintegrates, and I feel as lifeless and debilitated as I do on a boiling hot day. I sense your hand weighing on me 24/7.'

David knows God is just waiting for his confession, to take away the darkness of sin and to flood his life with light. 'Your iniquities have separated you from your God, your sins have hidden his face from you,' writes Isaiah (59:2). Although written centuries before Jesus is born, he knows for a fact it is the 'Redeemer' who will 'come to those who repent' (v.20).

Draw the cloud diagram and spend some time with God, asking (even writing) what sin is preventing you from enjoying his full peace, presence and power, and then thanking Jesus for his astonishing gift of forgiveness.

HELEN WILLIAMS

Wallow or worship

Have mercy on me, O God, according to your unfailing love; according to your great compassion blot out my transgressions. (NIV)

The wonderful thing about God is that he is not in the business of accusation or condemnation. He does not ask us to wallow in our sins or expect us to blame and punish ourselves. I read recently of a priest who, when asked what the most common problem he'd encountered in decades of hearing confession was, quite simply said, 'God.' He felt that very few of those coming to confession behaved as if God was a God of love, forgiveness, gentleness and compassion, rather that he was someone to cower before.

You may remember that the prodigal son rehearsed a confession for his father, but was his father interested in those carefully chosen words? No, he was so overjoyed his precious child had returned that he first ran to meet and embrace him (Luke 15:11–32).

In Psalm 51, penned as David returns to God after his devastating fall from grace with Bathsheba (2 Samuel 11—12), he begins with God's attributes. He speaks of God's unfailing love, great compassion, right judgement, righteousness and saving grace. I'm convinced that it's often as we worship God that the Holy Spirit gently convicts us of sin in our life and we find ourselves wanting to confess and put things right with God, in response to his goodness and love.

More often than not, our sin is not an explicitly evil thing, but simply our constant need or temptation to try and control our own lives. 'God is inviting us to take a holiday,' writes Philip Yancey (*Prayer*, Hodder, 2006), quoting Simon Tugwell: 'To stop being God for a while, and let him be God… We can stop doing all those important things we have to do in our own capacity as God and leave it to him to be God.' Challenging words!

The ancient Jesus Prayer proclaims who Jesus is and, in response to that truth, who I am in relation to him. It can be repeated emphasising different words: 'Lord Jesus Christ, Son of God, have mercy on me, a sinner.'

HELEN WILLIAMS

Let it all out!

Then I let it all out; I said, 'I'll make a clean breast of my failures to God.' Suddenly the pressure was gone – my guilt dissolved, my sin disappeared. These things add up. Every one of us needs to pray. (MSG)

Two years ago, I was asked to read Paul's hugely challenging but reassuring words in Romans 8 at a funeral. They speak of Jesus freeing us from condemnation and of the impossibility of anything separating us from his love. I stood in front of the coffin of a beautiful 28-year-old. It was devastatingly sad. Her husband and two-year-old daughter sat before me.

I gulped my way through the reading to its confident climax and then, seamlessly, a song started to play: 'Out of hiding (Father's song)'. There was not a dry eye in that chapel – we knew the absolute certainty of divine love and eternal destiny, but the challenge of vulnerability was written into everything that day.

It is honesty and vulnerability before God that the psalmist urges in Psalm 32. Clearly, something psychological as well as spiritual goes on when we articulate and confess our sin to him. There is release in the honesty.

In his book *Coming Close to Christ* (SPCK, 2009), Metropolitan Anthony tells of a prisoner he once visited in a London prison. 'You do not know what a relief it is to be found out,' the prisoner told him, 'now I have no need to hide who I am!' We're so good at pretending to ourselves, to our fellow Christians and to God that all is well. May God grant us freedom through our honesty today.

The song I mentioned is by Stephanie Gretzinger (Bethel Music) and, if you are able to, I recommend listening to it and using it as an act of submission to God who calls you out of hiding and into light.

HELEN WILLIAMS

A power shower

Wash away all my iniquity and cleanse me from my sin... Cleanse me with hyssop, and I shall be clean; wash me and I shall be whiter than snow. (NIV)

Having been confronted by Nathan, David lay on the ground for seven days and nights, without food, begging God for forgiveness and pleading for the life of the child he had fathered. He pleads with God to clean him, praying for the blotting out of his transgressions. He begs that God will wash (the Hebrew here is for washing clothes) away his iniquity and cleanse him from his sin.

He goes deeper too, praying for cleansing or purging with hyssop. He is probably referring to the ritual cleansing of lepers who had to be sprinkled seven times with sacrificial blood administered with a bunch of hyssop (the herb Syrian marjoram). Being washed whiter than snow probably refers to more ritual cleansing, necessary after touching a dead body (Numbers 19:16–19). This is serious repentance.

Travelling on dry dirt roads in Kenya, I often found myself covered in red dust. In one place I stayed there was a surprisingly powerful, hot, drenching shower from which I emerged deeply clean and refreshed at the end of each day. I sometimes ask God for this kind of cleansing, but I am aware that I'm quick to absorb society's messages about self-acceptance and self-love, often translating this mindset to my relationship with God. I forget that God set standards and put laws in place for the benefit of his people. I have only to check through the ten commandments to realise how easily I fall short of God's ideal.

In October 1904, a 26-year-old, Evan Roberts, stood up at a small prayer meeting in his Welsh village and invited the 17 people there to confess their sins and get rid of anything getting between them and God. What followed was miraculous, as thousands came to know Jesus in the Welsh Revival. Confession is powerful!

You could perhaps use water today as a symbol of confession and forgiveness – try dropping pebbles into a bowl of water as you let go of sins, or even just washing your hands for an extended time while praying for forgiveness.
HELEN WILLIAMS

Walk in the light

I said, 'I will confess my transgressions to the Lord.' And you forgave the guilt of my sin. Therefore let all the faithful pray to you… I will instruct you and teach you in the way you should go; I will counsel you. (NIV)

How then should we live, not wallowing in sin and failure but rejoicing in a right relationship with God? I love this challenge from one of the early church's boldest preachers (and Archbishop of Constantinople in the fifth century): 'Paul consoles his hearers by saying "renew yourselves" from day to day. This is what we do with houses: we keep constantly repairing them as they wear old. You should do the same thing to yourself. Have you sinned today? Have you made your soul old? Do not despair, do not despond, but renew your soul by repentance, and tears, and confession, and by doing good things. And never cease doing this' (St John Chrysostom).

You might imagine your life as a house with many rooms. One by one, invite the Holy Spirit to repair, sweep out and clean each room. It can be good to set aside time to do something like this, perhaps asking God to reveal anything in your past that might be in need of his forgiveness and healing too.

Both our psalms have a future aspect involving a change of heart and ongoing prayer. In Psalm 51 David goes right to the wellspring of his own life, asking for the miracle of a new, pure heart and a steadfast and willing spirit. Keep praying, he writes in Psalm 32, and God will protect and enfold you, becoming your 'hiding place' (no longer hiding from him).

Verses 8–9 shift to God's direct words in response to David's penitence. He promises to be our loving teacher, instructor and counsellor. Wow! Let's embrace this promise today! Some of God's clearest instructions about confession are in 1 John 1:5–10. It's all about walking 'in the light' as we allow the blood of Jesus to purify us. Do read this.

The prayer of Examen may be helpful – sitting in God's presence, letting the past day replay and asking the Holy Spirit to reveal your joy-filled, walking-in-the-light moments, but also where you were out of step with him.

HELEN WILLIAMS

My chains fell off

My tongue will sing of your righteousness. Open my lips, Lord, and my mouth will declare your praise. (NIV)

'My chains fell off; my heart was free!' wrote Charles Wesley. Our focus verses today deal with the glorious transformation that takes place after confession and forgiveness. When you are forgiven, says David in Psalm 32:1, you are 'blessed' (or 'happy') and surrounded (literally 'enfolded') by God's love and deliverance (vv.7, 10). The psalm then ends with an exhortation to rejoice, be glad and sing!

In Psalm 51 he describes the 'joy' of salvation (v. 12) and his natural response – to sing of God's righteousness (v. 14). He even asks: 'Open my lips, Lord, and my mouth will declare your praise.' I find myself asking whether I take Jesus' death and consequent forgiveness rather for granted. Does my gratitude lead to heartfelt praise and worship? David's joy and determination not to regress even spills over into a plan to tell others about God's mercy (v.13). It's interesting though that, while God totally forgives his sin, he doesn't remove the consequences (2 Samuel 12:18ff).

In Psalm 32:1 the Hebrew word translated 'forgiving' literally means 'carrying'. I remember a friend preaching about forgiveness and describing the women of a Ugandan village whom she frequently saw bent double under enormous loads of firewood. She spoke of the relief when their load was removed. They could stand straight again. This is what God does – he lifts off our guilt and invites us to walk tall.

David says God also covers our sin so that it can no longer be seen. He refuses to count our sins too, Jesus' death releasing us from our debt. Three 'C's – he has carried, covered and refused to count our sins, removing them 'as far as the east is from the west' (Psalm 103:12). Do I ever really internalise this? Am I apt to continue focusing on the sin and my unworthiness?

Try praying Psalm 103 out loud today. It's such a confident hymn of praise to our amazing God who utterly loves and utterly forgives.

HELEN WILLIAMS

Scapegoat

Therefore confess your sins to each other and pray for each other so that you may be healed. The prayer of a righteous person is powerful and effective. (NIV)

This week we have focused, with David, specifically on personal, private confession but, as the week closes, let's take a brief look at public and corporate confession. God gave specific instructions for public confession.

In Leviticus 16:20–22, the high priest was to confess the people's sins and then lay his hand on the head of a goat which would be sent off into the desert. This became the annual Day of Atonement. The scapegoat was such a graphic symbol of God's response to confession and his provision of a solution to sin. Of course, this was to be powerfully superseded by God's sacrifice of his own Son.

The Bible provides many examples of powerful public confession: there are accounts of Moses, Solomon, Nehemiah, Daniel, Hosea and others confessing the sins of the whole nation. Acts 19 tells the story of the sorcerers in Ephesus making a dramatic public confession, with the result that 'the word of the Lord spread widely and grew in power'. We read of the way sin affects whole communities – Achan (Joshua 7) and Ananias and Sapphira (Acts 5:1–11). Do we have some responsibility as Christians to confess the sins of our community, nation and world, and to pray for their healing?

For James, being in right relationship with others is vital. Mutual confession of how we have offended one another releases God's healing power. Of course, confession to one another needs handling with wisdom, some sinful thoughts being only for God's ears while practical steps to put things right are taken.

Praying a confession corporately as a church fellowship is powerful too. There are many published confession prayers which can be helpful when we don't know where to start – the Church of England website might be a useful resource. Fasting, like David, may accompany our confession too.

Read through our psalms again, maybe printing or copying them out, so you can highlight or underline things that feel important. If you have the means, listen to the incredible Allegri 'Miserere' (Psalm 51) as a prayer.

HELEN WILLIAMS

What the Bible says about itself

Elaine Storkey writes:

I began to read the Bible when I was four, before I even went to school. My father was in the navy and when he came home on leave, I rushed up to him, pointing to all the pages in Genesis that I had already completed. I still remember his somewhat deflating response as he unpacked his bags: 'So you read them, sweetheart, well done. But did you understand them?' I didn't. I wasn't even sure what most of the words meant. But I decided on the spot that one day I would! By the time I had become a committed Christian in my late teens, I had realised that the Bible was God's revelation to us and that it would take more than a lifetime to properly understand it.

2022 is the centenary year of BRF and it seems a good idea to take the opportunity to probe what the Bible says about itself. We can't do this, of course, by looking for the word 'Bible' in the biblical text. It's not there. The fourth century scholar John Chrysostom was probably the first to use that word when he took the Greek phrase *ta biblia* (the books) to refer to the writings of the Hebrew scriptures and the New Testament.

The Bible uses the word 'scripture' to refer to itself, although technically this applied first just to the Old Testament writings. The most common phrase for the Bible in the biblical text is 'the word of God', which can mean words spoken by God to his people, often through the law and the prophets, or written down in the Psalms and New Testament.

In three of the passages I have chosen, we find a reference to the 'mouth of God' – a metaphor suggesting that God is involved personally and intimately in communicating his word. All of these terms are widely accepted as referring to the Bible as God's revelation. They are interspersed in the different passages I have chosen from the Hebrew scriptures and New Testament.

Their authors lived centuries apart from each other, yet the claims they make for God's revelation are strikingly similar. Echoes resound in words that describe the power, truth, constancy, authenticity, wisdom and authority of the word of God. They all disclose a loving, creator God who reaches out to communicate to the people he has made.

God's word is eternal

Surely the people are grass. The grass withers, the flower fades, but the word of our God will stand forever. (ESV)

Sometimes the transience of human life hits us very strongly. Many years ago I went to a funeral of a teenage couple, killed in a motorcycle accident. The family weren't church members and wanted our curate to organise the service because he knew them from young people's gatherings.

The songs were poignant; the talk focused on the inestimable value of these two young people to God; friends and family spoke of the joy they'd brought to others during their brief time on earth. Their parents, consumed by grief, seemed numbed with shock. Yet as we followed them out of the church, one turned to express their gratitude for the support of hundreds of Christian believers. We had all shared their sorrow together.

By the end of the service, everyone had become sharply aware of the fragility of human existence. Though we might live a little longer than grass and flowers, we knew we were subject to the same process of death as the rest of creation.

Isaiah was writing to people who had also known sorrow and shared it together. More heartache was to come, including exile after a Babylonian conquest. Yet here he wanted to offer them comfort, based not on platitudes, but reality. His message was that although our life as mortals is transient, hope comes through God's word, for that stands forever.

God's word is a rock in our world. It is God's revelation to us. By God's word a world was made. Through God's word the prophets spoke. As God's word, Jesus came to live among us. God speaks into creation, into history and into our human hearts. And when we stand on God's word, we find a secure foundation, which lasts not just for our short lives, but for eternity.

Thank you, Lord, that your word endures forever. And thank you that we have been born again, 'not of perishable seed but of imperishable, through the living and abiding word of God' (1 Peter 1:23). Amen

ELAINE STORKEY

God's word is enlightening

Your word is a lamp for my feet, a light on my path. (NIV)

Have you ever stumbled around in the darkness, wondering where on earth you were going? In well-lit cities and homes, where sensors turn on lights whenever we move, we might find this rare. But for two friends of mine on a wild camping trip in a remote bit of Wales, the experience was quite a challenge. On the first evening, after spending two hours struggling through the darkness to find their way back to their tent, they resolved to give up exploring after the sun had gone down!

Light and darkness are key themes throughout the Bible, and their different associations would have been very familiar to earlier readers. Especially, the link between darkness and danger would have been immediately understood. Shepherds protecting flocks against predators, travellers fearing robbers on lonely roads or sailors steering boats through rock-strewn waters all faced challenges when darkness came.

The biblical focus on darkness is not simply on the absence of physical light, however. Darkness is also a metaphor for spiritual turmoil. For many biblical writers it is linked with sin and death. The people who 'walked in darkness' were not struggling with nightfall, but with great distress and fear. The only hope for this condition was that light would come to expose all that is evil and drive it away.

The light of God's word shines through all forms of darkness and guides us. In this verse, its light operates in two ways. As a lamp to our feet it is personal and immediate, enabling us to see all we need to see, as we take one step at a time. But as the light to our path it is directional and long-term, showing all of us who travel the best and safest way ahead.

Are there areas of your own life, or those of your family, which feel sometimes dark, or even dangerous? Why not pray about them now and ask God to shine light into the darkness.

ELAINE STORKEY

God's word is convicting

I have stored up your word in my heart, that I might not sin against you. (ESV)

We are very used to our culture seeing the heart as the centre of emotions and our romantic feelings. Think of the hundreds of love songs that have been written. But the biblical authors have a very different view. They see the heart as a metaphor for the spiritual centre of our lives and actions. The heart directs the will and governs our motives; it is where we make all the most crucial decisions in our lives.

That's why Proverbs 4:23 (NIV) urges us to 'above all else, guard your heart, for everything you do flows from it'. Jeremiah 17:9 wails that 'the heart is deceitful above all things and desperately sick'. The psalmist insists that the fool says in his heart (note, not his intellect) 'There is no God' (Psalm 14:1). In Luke 12:34, Jesus reminds us that where our treasure is, our hearts will be there also. And he blesses the 'pure in heart, for they shall see God' (Matthew 5:8). From these and other biblical passages, we get the picture of the deepest spiritual struggles taking place in our hearts.

The writer of this psalm is very aware of human failings. Most of us are, too. We share a persistent inclination to follow self-interest and can happily ignore the needs of others. But when the psalmist faces his tendency to disregard his own faults and bad attitudes, he knows it's wrong. It is sin against God.

The writer's response is therefore to fill his heart with God's word. That way he hears God and is strengthened to resist sin. We could do the same. When our thoughts and plans are shaped more by what God has shown us to be right, we also can find the willpower to resist the temptation of going in a wrong direction.

'Search me, God, and know my heart; test me and know my anxious thoughts. See if there is any offensive way in me, and lead me in the way everlasting' (Psalm 139: 23–24, NIV).

ELAINE STORKEY

God's word is true

Every word of God proves true; he is a shield to those who take refuge in him. Do not add to his words, lest he rebuke you and you be found a liar. (ESV)

About four years ago, the Oxford English Dictionary chose 'post-truth' as its word of the year. Since then, we have become increasingly used to a culture where truth does not seem to matter. We hear even world leaders making up their own version of reality and persuading huge crowds of followers to ignore all evidence to the contrary.

Listening to someone recently propounding completely fabricated myths as though they were verified facts, I realised with some dismay that lying no longer seems to be a matter of immorality; it is simply a process by which you get people to believe what you are saying.

Not 'bearing false witness' (lying) is the ninth commandment, and truth is the bedrock of the Christian faith. Our faith rests on the truth that Christ rose from the dead. If this is not true, then, as the apostle Paul points out, our belief is in vain. Jesus describes himself as 'the truth' in John 14:6, and tells us in John 8:32 that the truth will set us free. Truth is central, not just to our faith, but also as the basis for national and international affairs. If we lose truth in public life, then we have no way of deciding justice or building a good society.

In the Bible, truth is always associated with God. The Bible, God's word, discloses the truth about who we are, and how we should live. Here, in Proverbs, the writer paints a picture of God providing a shield against falsehood and a sanctuary against harm, offering refuge to those who seek it.

How much we need that protection today when lies abound everywhere! In the confusing and complex culture of our time, we need to hold on ever more firmly to God's word of truth.

Thank you, Lord, that the truth of your word persists through all ages, even when people reject it and lies abound in public places. Help me to be a truth-bearer for my generation. Amen

ELAINE STORKEY

God's word is powerful

'Is not my word like fire,' declares the Lord, 'and like a hammer that breaks the rock in pieces?' (NIV)

In this prophecy, Jeremiah conveys God's anger at the corrupt ways of his people's religious leaders. Idolatry, adultery, lies and all forms of godlessness are being passed off as though they have God's approval. False prophets encourage complacency as if it's from God. Echoing each other, they conspire to offer false hope, but fail utterly to sound the need for repentance and change. Into this ferment of hypocrisy and distortion, Jeremiah brings the reality of God's word.

Two similes simultaneously portray God's power and anger at such flagrant distortion. In the first picture, the word of God is like fire. We can picture red flames darting, heat consuming, devouring, burning up dross and rubbish, reducing objects of idol worship to ashes. Fire spreads quickly, often without warning. It cannot easily be contained and annihilates everything that it touches. Such a powerful image of the word of God soaks into our senses, impressing on us its swiftness and completeness in accomplishing what God sets out to do.

The second image portrays God's word in deliberate, slower terms. It is like a tool, a heavy hammer, with the very specific job of breaking up rocks and boulders. It needs strength to be wielded. It takes persistence to see the job through. Yet it will prevail. Rocks of falsehood, evil, religious lies, immorality, in fact anything which lies in the way of truth will be hammered to smithereens by the power of God's word.

These images challenge us today not to underestimate the word of God but to recognise its strength. We are urged to pray and share the Bible with others, and then see it work. God will use his word to convict people's hearts. Releasing its power can eradicate forces in our world that undermine God's truth, authority and love.

How have you experienced the power of God's word over these last few weeks? Are there areas where you need God to empower you? Ask God to remove anything in your life which holds his power back.

ELAINE STORKEY

God's word is purposeful

'So shall my word be that goes out from my mouth; it shall not return to me empty, but it shall accomplish that which I purpose, and shall succeed in the thing for which I sent it.' (ESV)

Words play many roles in human interaction. Positively, they might make us laugh, impart information, give encouragement, share insights, entertain, challenge, rebuke and convey love. Negatively, they can hurt, scorn, share gossip, bully, demean, undermine and destroy. Sometimes, words make very little impact because they are empty. At other times they are the catalyst to address injustice and bring change.

In this prophecy Isaiah compares the pointless things we say and do with those that are satisfying and meaningful, and urges us to do the latter. We need to rely on God more to find out how. Of course, Isaiah acknowledges that what God accomplishes is enormously different from what we can do. God is God; his thoughts and ways are very different from ours. Yet, the more we seek and understand God's purposes, the more likely we are to live a purposeful existence ourselves.

God's communication is always purposeful. When God speaks, his word doesn't simply evaporate into thin air. Nor does it just sound back to him like an empty echo. Isaiah pictures God's word as active and busy, getting on with the job God has given it to do. He likens it to rain and snow falling to the ground. This happens for a purpose. Rain comes to water the ground, nourish the roots of plants and swell the growing grain. When it accomplishes its object, earth creatures are fed. In a similar way, when God's word fulfils its purpose, the whole of creation is blessed.

God sees the impact of his word on our lives. He knows when we allow it to sustain and build us up together in Christ's peace and love. When it empowers us to live more effectively as citizens of God's kingdom, then it will indeed have succeeded in doing what God has purposed.

Lord, help us to see where your purposes are being accomplished in the world around us. Please increase our desire to work with you so that our words might reflect your word in their witness to your love. Amen

ELAINE STORKEY

God's word is wise

For the Lord gives wisdom; from his mouth come knowledge and understanding. (NIV)

Have you ever felt completely out of your depth? Perhaps, like me, you've faced situations where you simply haven't known what to do or say next. In these times I've learnt to pray quickly for wisdom, and then waited for God to show me how to respond.

There's nothing wrong with being out of our depth. Human understanding often just isn't adequate. In fact, you could say it makes us more ready to be dependent on God. God's word encourages us into that dependency. Even more, it suggests that when we know we lack wisdom, God the Holy Spirit sometimes gives it to us in abundance.

Someone calculated that 'wisdom' is mentioned 222 times in the Old Testament, and many of those references are in the book of Proverbs. In Proverbs 2 the writer talks of wisdom protecting us and helping us to avoid pitfalls in our lives. Wisdom safeguards us from falling into bad company or being lured into sin. Wisdom is necessary for us all.

In our passage, wisdom comes from the mouth of God. It is in God's spoken word. People down the centuries have found wisdom in the Bible, which has laid a foundation for their own understanding. This has been true not only for theologians, but also for students of literature, poetry, psychology, history, sociology, politics and science. Jan Swammerdam, a 17th-century Dutch scientist, looked down his microscope and exclaimed, 'The glory of God in the body of a louse.' And many early scientists believed they were thinking God's thoughts after him.

This is not about seizing on individual Bible texts but developing a whole biblical worldview. Those who read God's word and invite wisdom into their hearts find that God indeed helps them to be wise.

Let's give thanks to God for the many leading scientists and scholars who are Christian believers. Perhaps you can reflect on how God's word can be the foundation for your work and relationship with others.

ELAINE STORKEY

God's word is life-sustaining

Jesus answered, 'It is written, "Man shall not live on bread alone, but on every word that comes from the mouth of God."' (NIV)

Jesus quotes scripture at the devil when he is tempted in the wilderness. He's hungry, having fasted for 40 days, and Satan challenges him to satisfy hunger by turning stones into bread. Jesus uses the authority of God's word in Deuteronomy 8:3 to rebuke Satan and reassert the priorities of his ministry. He knows already he will have to go through suffering; there can be no shortcuts.

It is a good reminder for us. We can become so focused on our material and physical needs that we get priorities wrong. It's easy to believe our lives would be richer, happier or altogether more pleasant if we just had the things we want. Yet we can become materially full and spiritually empty. The wrong 'food' can't satisfy our hungry hearts. We need to receive God's word and God's will, if we are going to grow into healthy, whole people.

It's apt that Jesus refers to 'every word' from God's mouth. For the Bible has many diverse forms of words: history, law, prophecy, songs, proverbs, biography, letters. Yet running through them all is the unity of God's revelation. From the Bible we learn who God is and what it is to be human; we understand more about God's relationship with us and how to live. Feeding on God's word encourages and challenges us.

By saying not bread 'alone', Jesus isn't denying people's physical needs. We're not to forego the basic things of life but enjoy the gifts of creation: God rarely asks us to become ascetics. The danger is when we become fixated on these things and put our trust in them. Ultimately, that leads to idolatry. If Satan could tempt Jesus, he can certainly tempt us to materialist worship. But God's word still empowers us and will see the devil off.

In Jeremiah 15:16 the prophet says, 'When your words came, I ate them; they were my joy and heart's delight.' What kinds of pictures might you use to describe what it is like to feed on the word of God?

ELAINE STORKEY

God's word is Christ-disclosing

'You search the Scriptures because you think that in them you have eternal life; and it is they that bear witness about me.' (ESV)

The gospel of John records many disputes Jesus had with the religious leaders. Here, they are questioning his authority because he has just performed a miracle on the sabbath. In challenging their legalism, Jesus points out their distorted view of the scriptures, and their failure to recognise the promised Messiah is now with them in person.

It is far too easy for any of us to have a distorted view of the Bible. We can easily take texts out of context and fail to understand them. We can elevate the passages about law and downplay the teachings of grace. We can miss the underlying narratives of creation, sin and redemption, which run through the Bible and open it up for us. We can fail to grasp that the Hebrew scriptures must be understood through the lens of the New Testament.

These religious leaders are Bible scholars, but they've not properly understood their law and prophets. If they had read them with open hearts, they would have made the spiritual connection between their prophesies and the miracles that Jesus was performing. Instead, they become judgemental and agitated because this miracle occurred on the sabbath. They miss the bigger revelation that Jesus is the one foretold and the Lord of the sabbath.

The unity of God's word is in Jesus. He is the embodiment of the word of God. Christ is the 'Logos', the 'Word made flesh' who dwelt among us, as John tells us so eloquently in his gospel (John 1). He is the one before all things and in whom all things hold together (Colossians 1:17). The whole of the New Testament rests on the centrality of Christ as the incarnate Word. And as his followers, we can read the Bible with rejoicing and thanksgiving.

Lord, thank you that the scriptures bear witness to Jesus. Please deepen my knowledge and discipleship so that I am never in danger of missing the miracles that you perform around me. Amen

ELAINE STORKEY

God's word is authentic

And we also thank God constantly for this, that when you received the word of God, which you heard from us, you accepted it not as the word of men but as what it really is, the word of God, which is at work in you believers. (ESV)

Two years ago an interview with a young woman made headlines in Scotland after her father was sent to prison for historic sexual abuse. She had suffered enormously throughout her childhood because her parents were members of a religious cult which encouraged 'free love'. The founder of the cult was quoted as teaching that God was love and love was sex, so there should be no limits regardless of age or relationship.

Most cults throughout history have led people seriously astray. The process usually does not happen all at once, but is a long, slow slide into heresy and apostasy, with very dangerous consequences. Over time, magnetic cult leaders become so influential that their followers accept their words as equal in authority to the Bible, ultimately surpassing it.

When the apostle Paul wrote to the church in Thessalonica, he was aware that counterfeit teachers could easily gain followers through their words. Writing to the Christians at Thessalonica, he expresses gratitude that they recognised what they were receiving from the apostle were not his words but was indeed the word of God.

So how could they discern that? Paul's Christ-centred teaching was the key: his constant focus on Jesus and his sacrificial love. Another mark of authenticity was his stress on the implications of Christ's self-giving in the lives of believers. Care for one another, the unity of the body, protection for the vulnerable, repentance and new life were all truly identified as God's word for the early church.

The Bible speaks about its own authenticity and many biblical authors witness to the truth of God's word. But its validity is shown most powerfully in the lives of people who believe it. As that word is at work in us, may God give us grace to show the evidence in our lives.

Father, we pray today for all those precious women harmed by people who have claimed to be acting in your name. We ask for your protection on the vulnerable and that those who distort your truth will be brought to justice. Amen
ELAINE STORKEY

God's word is penetrating

For the word of God is living and active, sharper than any two-edged sword, piercing to the division of soul and of spirit, of joints and of marrow, and discerning the thoughts and intentions of the heart. (ESV)

I was in an antiquarian bookshop when some old volumes were brought in from an elderly, downsizing Cambridge academic. I was interested to see a Bible included. It looked like many others of its day – thin paper, small print, with an old black cover. Its owner saw my glance. 'It's old,' he said, 'but not dead.'

He was right. The word of God is alive and effective, whatever physical form contains it. It is intrinsically connected to God, the source of life and power. The writer to the Hebrews pictures God's word as a sword, sharp on both its edges. It is active and can penetrate very deeply – through a hard bony surface to the soft marrow below. Or it can pierce through our exterior, surface life to our spiritual motives and commitments beneath.

In this metaphor, God's living and active word can open up to us what we are really like. It can see beyond our pretence, challenge our denial and uncover our true selves. God's Spirit can reveal to us our thoughts and intentions, our values and shortcomings. The image also suggests that the process can be an excruciating one. Cutting through bone and flesh is fine for a post-mortem; but on someone alive, the pain might be overwhelming.

This has, in fact, been the experience of many people who have allowed God's word to search their hearts and penetrate their inner being. It's not unusual to hear of people weeping, convicted of their sin against God, recognising the hurt and harm they have caused to others. Yet the wonderful thing is that when God's word undertakes this process for us, we need no anaesthetic. For God is ready to forgive and heal, and invite us into a new wholeness with him.

Thank you, God, that you know me better than I know myself. Help me to confront the sins in my life and allow your forgiveness and healing to make me the person you want me to be. Amen

ELAINE STORKEY

God's word is authoritative

All Scripture is breathed out by God and profitable for teaching, for reproof, for correction, and for training in righteousness. (ESV)

The writer of this passage was talking about the Hebrew scriptures because the New Testament was yet to come. But we recognise it applies equally to the whole Bible. He pictures God breathing out words for us to breathe in, and giving the Bible authority. While human writers with different personalities write the words down, God is the ultimate source of what they write.

Scripture is defined as 'profitable'. By that, the writer means the time we spend in study brings added value and reward. This value comes in four ways. The first is teaching. The Bible puts down foundations for understanding God, creation, values, human life, meaning and purpose. We soak ourselves in scripture and become more equipped to learn.

The second is reproof. The Bible moves from the story of creation to that of sin and exposes evil in all its ugly manifestations. We learn what is wrong with the world: that sin is personal, alienating, addictive and destructive. We're helped to identify sins in ourselves, in our society and in its institutions.

The third is correction. The Bible does not leave sin as the problem but points to the solution. It shows redemption promised and fulfilled in the sacrificial death of Jesus. Forgiveness follows repentance and faith, and brings the glorious possibility of a new, radical future.

Fourth is learning to live well. The Bible offers a spiritual training course, where, with the Holy Spirit's guidance, we can begin to overcome the impact of sin in our world and bring hope.

The passage is brief, but its truths are so weighty. We are drawn into the authority of the Bible over our lives, and the spiritual power it offers us. May this word flourish in our lives and in our outreach to others.

Lord God, thank you for not leaving us to follow our own ideas or those of other people in seeking how to live. Thank you that you have given us your word. May we follow its wisdom and be blessed by its power. Amen

ELAINE STORKEY

God's word is challenging

Preach the word; be prepared in season and out of season; correct, rebuke and encourage – with great patience and careful instruction. (NIV)

A student training for ministry was sent on placement to a very traditional church. As her tutor, I needed to assess her first sermon, so I phoned the vicar to fix a date for her preaching. 'Oh, as a woman she won't be preaching,' he explained. 'She'll just be sharing her thoughts on the Bible reading for the day.' I didn't bother to quibble, and turned up to hear her deliver a very fine sermon.

Whatever we call it, Christians are called to teach and preach. The Bible is to be communicated to the church and beyond. In this passage the task is given to Timothy, a young man mentored by the apostle Paul, and a leader and evangelist in the church at Ephesus. The instructions given to him are just as relevant to us today.

Like Timothy, we must preach the Bible, not just our ideas, and be faithful to the passage. This means we need to study it ourselves first so we can offer 'careful instruction'. And we have to do that 'in season and out of season', in other words, whether we feel like it or not! Preachers serve people best when their words open up God's word to make it available. So, where the passage corrects or rebukes us, we must let that be heard. Where it offers encouragement, we must share it wholeheartedly.

Perhaps you're reading this and thinking, 'but I'm not a preacher'. Yet we can all share the Bible. It's often only inhibition or lack of practice that stops us. Most of us could teach Bible stories to children, or post a verse on Facebook, or share a passage we've read with a friend. If you take the challenge and reach out, it might just be the start of faith for someone else.

Are you using all the gifts that God has given you in your Christian life? Ask God if you have gifts of communication or outreach which you have not yet identified, and which you can begin to use in his kingdom.

ELAINE STORKEY

81

God's word is faithful

Jesus performed many other signs in the presence of his disciples, which are not recorded in this book. But these are written that you may believe that Jesus is the Messiah, the Son of God, and that by believing you may have life in his name. (NIV)

We are often selective when we read the Bible and have our favourite verses. We should never lose the 'big picture' of the whole biblical story, but there is nothing wrong in selecting passages that help us most. In fact, the books of the Bible are themselves selective. They focus on what God most wants us to hear.

In these verses John makes that very clear. He's not writing a complete account of everything Jesus said and did. As he muses in chapter 21, the world probably wouldn't be big enough to contain it all! He relies on the Holy Spirit to direct him to the specific things about Jesus that God wants him to pass on. His key task is not to produce a comprehensive account, but a faithful one.

This is true of the whole Bible. It doesn't tell the story of the world, the universe and everything. But it is faithful in recounting what God wants to communicate to us. It speaks of God, of God's relationship with creation and ourselves. It highlights the journeys of faith and unbelief of God's people and God's redemptive love in Jesus. The Bible is God's faithful revelation which invites us into faith.

John's motive for writing his gospel is explicitly evangelistic. He wants to show Jesus is indeed the anointed one, the Son of God. He draws on the Hebrew scriptures – the law and the prophets, the promises and the Psalms – and lays the evidence before us so that we will believe and find life in Christ's name. Billions of people throughout history have read John's faithful gospel and put their trust in Christ. May we pray that generations to come will do the same.

Lord, I thank you for the gospel writers in recording faithfully the life and death of Jesus, and for the power of their testimony through all ages. Thank you that I do believe and can indeed have life in his name. Amen

ELAINE STORKEY

Knowing God's rest

Di Archer writes:

Rest. There's a thing. If only I knew how to do it well. Why doesn't it come naturally? Why do I get in a muddle with it – no matter what season of my life I am in? Why is it so hard to get a healthy pace of life and stick to it?

The concept of knowing God's rest feels very challenging. Oh, certainly, I know that it is a significant biblical theme. I know that becoming a Jesus-follower in my teens changed my attitudes to everything, including what I did with my 'own time'. I like the growing understanding in general society that we all need 'me time' and 'down time'. For those of us in the UK, our inherited Protestant work ethic was due for some nuancing – we have the longest work hours in Europe and balancing that up a bit is good. Recognising that we are made for input as well as output is surely a well-being idea that we can applaud.

But God's rest – is that different? How does it relate to our work–life balance conversations? Is there a difference between feeling well-rested, say, at the end of a holiday or happy weekend, and the 'rest' that is part of our relationship with God?

We all start in different places, of course, and that's fine. It may be that you can barely find the time to read this because you are surrounded by the incessant demands of a young family. It may be that you are wondering how to fill your time, because that's how it is at the moment. Or anywhere in between.

However, my experience says that, no matter where we are now, so many of us have trouble finding real rest – spiritual, emotional and physical. In that vivid story of Jesus in the home of Mary and Martha, where Jesus commends Mary for taking the role of a disciple and sitting and listening to him, rather than Martha, who is running around like a headless chicken trying to get everything done – so many of us relate more easily to Martha and not to Mary. And we feel a bit put out by Jesus seemingly taking Mary's side. Someone has to get everything done, don't they? Someone has to feed everyone, and sort everything, hold it all together?

How, then, to actually know God's rest?

The beginning

So the creation of the heavens and the earth and everything in them was completed. On the seventh day God had finished his work of creation, so he rested from all his work. And God blessed the seventh day and declared it holy, because it was the day when he rested from all his work of creation. (NLT)

As we explore what God's rest might mean for each of us, we start at the beginning. For the idea of rest is there, within the first few verses of the Genesis story. However we understand the creation-versus-evolution debate, let us assume that the Bible knows what it is talking about and that, somehow or another, God made the world. And then he rested.

But why? Why did God rest? Surely he wasn't tired? Presumably, he could have spent all seven of the days he had just made in creating things. Why spend one of his sparkling new days in rest? Fascinating. It's also fascinating that this pattern works for the whole of humankind. The six days on and one day off has stood us in good stead. We are made in God's image, and that includes the ability to rest. The world turns on a seven-day cycle, and woe betide us if one of those days is not rest of some sort. We burn out, crash out and cannot function without rest.

Genesis tells us that resting is what God does. He did not invent it just for us. He rests, it's in his nature. He created, he looked at it all, and saw that it was spectacular, and he responded by resting. And he made us to be like him.

Not only that, but he declared the seventh day to be 'holy' (Genesis 2:3) and he actually blessed that day. He made it special and different. God's day for rest is part of his good creation. It is not just there so we can survive and rejuvenate; rest enables us to enjoy holiness and blessing. It is there so we can breathe, remember God and see the good around us.

If God can rest, then we can too. In what ways can you find some rest today?
DI ARCHER

To rest is the law!

'Remember to observe the Sabbath day by keeping it holy. You have six days each week for your ordinary work, but the seventh day is a Sabbath day of rest dedicated to the Lord your God. On that day no one in your household may do any work.' (NLT)

Having seen that rest is integral to the nature of God, and our nature too, what does this mean for us that God set aside a special day for it? Let's follow the trail in the Bible story. By the second book of the Bible, God's chosen people, the Israelites, were a nomadic tribe wandering the wilderness, working out who they were and what their unique contract with the God of the universe might mean.

To assist them, God gave them the ten commandments, which helped to define their identity and how they would relate to God, themselves and each other. The eighth commandment is our verse focus for today. It is pretty explicit. In contrast to the surrounding nations, the Israelites had a day that was to be dedicated to their God – because he had made them and because he gave them this day as a special, good and wonderful day to rest. Once a week, they were to down tools, even the servants, livestock and foreigners. A true day of rest.

Oh, how we have tangled ourselves in knots trying to 'keep the Sabbath day holy'. Does 'no work' mean following the Jewish example and preparing everything for the sabbath during the previous day so that rest really happens – even the food? How can this work for those with little ones and babies? Should we be obeying the Jewish 39 sabbath rules?

Surely God's rest means something other than this? That first day of rest God had reads like it was a very happy day – a day of rejoicing and laughter over a good creation. It is this God to whom we dedicate our sabbaths.

How do you currently celebrate your sabbath day of rest? What does it mean to you to dedicate it to God?

DI ARCHER

Slaves cannot rest

Observe the Sabbath day by keeping it holy… Remember that you were once slaves in Egypt, but the Lord your God brought you out with his strong hand and powerful arm. That is why the Lord your God has commanded you to rest on the Sabbath day. (NLT)

At first glance, this could look similar to yesterday's reading. However, Moses was revisiting the commandments some 40 years after he first received them from God. Clearly, the community needed to look at them again. The interesting thing is the difference from the time before.

This time, commandment number eight had an addition: a robust reminder that God had rescued the whole nation from slavery. Now, not only was the call to rest based on God's act of creation and his own resting, but it was also linked to his bringing Israel out from bondage in Egypt.

Was this a timely reminder because the nomadic tribe was actually starting to win territory from others, on the east side of the Jordan? Were they tempted by success to forget that they would not have been there at all if God had not brought them out from Egypt?

It seems to be one of the easiest things to do, this forgetting of God and what he has done. We get distracted, discouraged and absorbed in the current moment. We, too, can be charmed by success. We can mislay our history. Like the Israelites, we have an astounding tale of rescue, even greater than liberation from an oppressing nation.

We have been set free in Jesus from the slavery of sin, hopelessness and godlessness. We have a purpose. We are loved. We have eternal security. We know the creator God personally – we are not even dependent on keeping the ten commandments, or a tier of priests interceding for us. Jesus has done it all for us. We have the potential to live a Spirit-filled, Jesus-led, God-worshipping life. Yet still we forget!

This is why we need a day of rest. To remember him.

Dear Father, help me to enjoy remembering you in all you have done to set me free. Thank you! Amen

DI ARCHER

It's a gift

And I gave them my Sabbath days of rest as a sign between them and me. It was to remind them that I am the Lord, who had set them apart to be holy. But the people of Israel rebelled … They also violated my Sabbath days. (NLT)

Now we are diving into a later era in the history of the Israelites, when they were far from the promised land they had called home. The majority of them were in exile in Babylon. And on a precise day (14 August 591 BC), some of the leaders came to the prophet Ezekiel, hoping for an encouraging word from their God. Instead, they received what can only be described as a proper pasting.

Again and again, in among the anguished fury of God's catalogue of their failings, was the oft-repeated reference to their trashing of the sabbath.

Why did this matter so much? Because God had given the sabbath as a gift to his people. It was not a burden to be resisted – it was a present. And like the other gifts that God had lavished on his people – rescue from slavery, a beautiful, bountiful land to live in, the revealed presence of God – the Israelites had taken it for granted. They forgot God.

It is so easy to see how the Israelites messed things up for themselves. It is harder to acknowledge when we do the same. Do we trust God's gift of rest enough to receive it? When do we turn to idols and disobedience? Can I trust that, if I stop worrying at my work for a sabbath day, he will take care of it and me? Can I trust my time to him – that he will give me what I need? Can I release those jobs that scream at me and turn my heart's attention to God? Can I calm my panic and let him order my days? Can I take my foot off the pedal of my ambition for a day? To rest in God is to rest in trust.

Read Proverbs 16:1–3. Dear Father, I need you to help me here. My trust levels go up and down. Please may I rest in the truth that you do know best. Amen
DI ARCHER

Burning the candle at both ends?

It is useless for you to work so hard from early morning until late at night, anxiously working for food to eat; for God gives rest to his loved ones. (NLT)

In case you thought that God approves of us working all hours, this psalm is another reminder that we are built for rest as well. Written for pilgrims as they approached Jerusalem, this song of worship has as its focus a bedrock trust in the goodness and faithfulness of God. It encourages us to put God first in all things.

What is the point of doing anything, it says, unless God is involved? We can stress and strive, but God is God, and he will have the first and last word. All blessing and protection ultimately come from him. We are not in final control of life – he is.

In this psalm, this is particularly seen in the gift of children. Thousands of years later we still feel the same. Despite the advances in medicine, the miracle of birth is still an awesome thing. Whether or not we have our own children, or whatever we have been through in this issue, we continue to regard them as a gift.

Perhaps they are the most pertinent example of our helplessness in the face of the mystery of life, death and existence. We are a dependent creation. We did not make ourselves. It is all gift. Acknowledging God and recognising our dependence is the way to live, says this psalmist. You are God-made and he knows what you need, and this includes rest.

If you are facing a season where rest seems nigh-on impossible, take a few moments today to talk to your heavenly Father about it. Take him at his word and remind him and yourself that he has promised rest to you. Ask him to give it to you, perhaps in ways you have never thought of before. He loves you. He gives rest to those he loves.

Dear Father, it is so hard to dial down enough to rest when there is so much on my mind. Please help me to find the ways of rest you have promised me. Amen

DI ARCHER

Perfectionism?

One Sabbath day as Jesus was walking through some grainfields, his disciples began breaking off heads of grain to eat. But the Pharisees said to Jesus, 'Look, why are they breaking the law by harvesting grain on the Sabbath?' (NLT)

What did Jesus say about rest? He seemed to have a whole new attitude to the Jewish law, unlike that of any other rabbi at the time, so how did he treat the sabbath? As we have seen, the religious leaders had a particular interest in this, debating and deciding on detailed rules for the sabbath in order to keep the law of rest. It soon became obvious to them that Jesus was not toeing the line. Jesus' disciples 'harvesting' the grain as they walked could technically be called work, which was not allowed. Ditto the healing by Jesus of the man with a deformed hand in the next story.

Writer Mark says that the Pharisees were aiming to catch Jesus out and build up evidence against him to prove he was not a proper Jew. But Jesus was on another page altogether. I get the impression that he laughed as he tried to remind those leaders that the sabbath was supposed to be a gift for us, not a burden. He even quoted the esteemed King David, who broke the sabbath rules in a time of necessity. Clearly the disciples did not fear a reprimand from Jesus.

However, when the leaders hesitated to approve of his healing of the man, that provoked a different reaction in Jesus. He was angry and sad. How could the leaders be so rule-bound that they had lost their compassion? Even worse, how could they have thought that God's compassion for the hurting and needy was similarly limited?

Yes, we all do it. We do it to ourselves, and we do it to others. God's ways of living are meant for health, not restriction. But we twist them round, set up impossible standards and then pronounce judgement.

Read Mark 2:27 again. Imagine what it was like to be walking in the grainfield with Jesus. Yes, says his smile. Sabbath rest is for you. You can take what you need today.

DI ARCHER

Saying 'no'

Immediately after this, Jesus insisted that his disciples get back into the boat and cross to the other side of the lake, while he sent the people home. After sending them home, he went up into the hills by himself to pray. Night fell while he was there alone. (NLT)

It would be so nice if rest were handed to us on a plate. Sometimes it is, of course. But it is more likely that we have to follow Jesus' example and fight for it. Those three intense years of Jesus' ministry are exhausting just to read. Living them must have been extraordinarily demanding. Yet again and again, Jesus carved out time to rest and rejuvenate (see Luke 5:16).

In this chapter, he twice claims space on his own to recuperate. The first time, it was because he heard the miserable news of his cousin John's beheading. Jesus needed to be alone to grieve and come to terms with that. His time was limited to a boat ride, however, because the crowds of people wanting help and healing were waiting when he landed. His outstanding compassion for them met them in their need, as he healed and then fed them.

Not surprising, then, that he tried again to have some alone time afterwards. He sent his disciples away and stayed behind for prayer and fellowship with God. Notwithstanding that this prayer space was followed by the astounding miracle of walking on the water, when yet again his disciples found themselves in totally uncharted waters of faith, Jesus did need and take the time for rest. I can imagine that the disciples had tried to persuade him to come with them.

Fighting for time to rest as Jesus did means saying no to others on occasions. Such a hard thing to do well, but so worth it. The alternatives are resentment and exhaustion. It also means saying yes to God – for the absolute best rest we can get is the one that restores us spiritually as well as emotionally, physically and mentally.

Read Mark 6:30–31. What restores you spiritually, and how can you make space for more?

DI ARCHER

Resting and partying

One day some people said to Jesus, 'John the Baptist's disciples fast and pray regularly, and so do the disciples of the Pharisees. Why are your disciples always eating and drinking?' (NLT)

I suppose we obey rules to keep ourselves safe. Maybe some of those religious leaders had their hearts in the right place – they genuinely wanted to do the correct things for the sake of their relationship with God. Jesus must have seemed such a maverick to them. What did he think he was doing, breaking the rules and not preserving the order they worked so hard at? Why, for example, were his disciples not fasting regularly, twice a week, like they did? This was a good thing to do, right?

Jesus' answer was extraordinary. He completely sidestepped the implicit condemnation about rule-keeping and instead talked about himself. He did not do that often. But he changed the context here, deliberately referring to his presence as a cause for celebration – and therefore also food and drink in joyful abundance. Just like his first miracle in John's gospel, when Jesus rescued a wedding by supplying high-quality wine, he affirmed the party spirit. He also challenged his listeners to allow change to come – no one would dream of putting new wine into old wineskins after all. Resting with Jesus includes partying!

In our food-obsessed society today, we have managed to make the issues around it even more complicated than they were then. Some of us have lots of food – but have no idea how to eat it for health. Some of us have little food – and the struggle to find it takes the joy away. Most of us have separated it from our relationship to God; we do not even say thank you for it before we partake. So today, in recognition of God's grace, provision and restoration, how can we eat and drink as grateful, restful disciples?

There is a big feast waiting for us in heaven. Let's learn how to enjoy the taste of it now.

Read Matthew 8:11. You are welcome at the big kingdom feast!

DI ARCHER

91

Total rest

God saved you by his grace when you believed. And you can't take credit for this; it is a gift from God. Salvation is not a reward for the good things we have done, so none of us can boast about it. For we are God's masterpiece. (NLT)

So far, we have looked at rest in the story of the Bible before Jesus' death and resurrection. We have seen how rest is a good gift for us. So what difference does it make that Jesus is alive today? To be honest, it is implicit in all we have considered so far, but let's explore further.

In his letter to the church in Ephesus, the apostle Paul expresses his excitement and conviction that it is the grace of God that changes everything. In these meaning-rich verses, he underlines that it is all gift, it is all grace. We have not done anything ourselves; God in Jesus has done it all.

What a relief! There are so many days when I get anxious about how well or otherwise I am doing, or beat myself up for things done or undone. I have many rabbit holes on these themes that I have lost myself down over the years. But here is the truth: God loved me enough to rescue me through what Jesus has done; it is not my doing at all. I don't even have to take responsibility for 'believing properly'. God has even given that as a gift to me. I am okay because God says I am.

This is why we can rest. The rest that God offers is all-encompassing. It covers everything, from a walk in the countryside to the most precious encounter with God we have ever had; from relaxing, playing or feasting with friends, to the satisfaction of letting your mind wander after a focused day. We can rest because he has given us utter peace with him. We do not have to fight for ourselves. We are loved just as we are. More than that – he thinks we are brilliant: his masterpiece.

If you are not sure that you have been saved by God's grace, pray about it today and find someone to talk to. Otherwise: rejoice. Even on a bad hair day, you are a work of art.

DI ARCHER

Can we have soul rest?

Jesus said, 'Come to me, all of you who are weary and carry heavy burdens, and I will give you rest. Take my yoke upon you. Let me teach you, because I am humble and gentle at heart, and you will find rest for your souls. For my yoke is easy to bear, and the burden I give you is light.' (NLT)

Jesus really understands that we get exhausted. He has been there. He invited people to 'take his yoke' because he could see the enormous mental and spiritual burdens they were carrying. He was very well aware that many were refusing his message and turning against him, despite the compassionate miracles he was performing and how confusing that was for everyone – even his cousin John the Baptist. The latter had sent a message from prison, asking him if he was the Messiah. Jesus' response was to say: tell John what you see I am doing. Then he commended those who had a more childlike attitude, for they were far more likely to see him for who he was.

We do not have to be clever or intellectual or of theological bent to take Jesus' yoke. It is there for us all, no matter who we are or what we do. It is an invitation that is easily understood by those of a straight-forward, believing faith – the sort of faith that takes Jesus at his word.

Jesus says: 'I can see you are worn out in so many ways. Come close to me and let me give you rest.' How incredible that we have a Saviour who is gentle and humble. How extraordinary! Our burdens may be self-imposed or put upon us by others and life, but it does not matter. Jesus will help us to walk in step with him so that he takes the load. He promises true rest.

I suspect that I have all too often missed out on this wonderful invitation, determined to 'do it myself' or too blinded by tiredness to respond to his kind presence. Today is the day for a small step towards his way of doing things.

Dear Jesus, forgive me for ignoring your kindness. Help me to receive your gift of rest for my soul, even today. Amen

DI ARCHER

Balanced rest

So there is a special rest still waiting for the people of God. For all who have entered into God's rest have rested from their labours, just as God did after creating the world. So let us do our best to enter that rest. But if we disobey God, as the people of Israel did, we will fall. (NLT)

I once heard understanding the truths of the Bible described as being like riding a bicycle. In order to stay upright, you need to pedal with both feet, one at a time, and that way you keep your balance. We are completely dependent on the grace of God for the restoration of our relationship with him. It is all grace, and all gift.

The rest that he offers is so much more than relaxing at the weekend – it is peace with God; it is soul rest. It is having access to the peace that passes all understanding (Philippians 4:7), that no one can know without being a friend of God. It is looking forward to a future with a loving God, both now and beyond death.

However, it looks like the writer to the Hebrews is contradicting this. He suggests that, just as a whole generation of Israelites missed out on entering their 'rest' of the promised land because of disobedience, so can we. He exhorts us to look after our faith, not taking it or God for granted, but being 'careful' (3:12) with our hearts. Following Jesus does not take away our capacity to choose. We have myriad opportunities every day to make choices that either turn us towards God or away from him. Be warned, says Hebrews, don't lose what is promised.

But just before panic sets in, another turn of the bicycle wheel brings us to the closing verses of the chapter, where we are reminded that Jesus is there to help us. We can rush into his presence, knowing we will be met with grace and mercy just when we need it. Even if we do fall off, he is always there to pick us up, dust us down and help us to get going again.

Thank you, God, that you are always there for me, no matter what. Help me to rest in the power of your presence and promises. Amen

DI ARCHER

You really are loved

Even before he made the world, God loved us and chose us in Christ to be holy and without fault in his eyes. God decided in advance to adopt us into his own family by bringing us to himself through Jesus Christ. This is what he wanted to do, and it gave him great pleasure. (NLT)

Who are you? If you described yourself in one sentence, what would you say? Would you refer to your character, your job or your relationships? Or perhaps the way you look or how you feel? Or even, that you are a Christian.

On the inside, though, what do you really believe about yourself? These opening verses of Paul's letter to the Ephesians are the most mind-blowing descriptions of who you actually are; of who I am. Paul's words tumble over themselves as he strives to convey the truths which will set us free to be all that we were made and redeemed for. Even before you were a twinkle in anyone's eye, you were loved and chosen by a good, glorious, creator God.

You are not a mistake. You are deeply loved, always and forever, and you have nothing to prove. It gives God joy to have you in his amazing family. You are not defined by your history, your parentage, your struggles, your limitations or your ups and your downs. Your identity is carried deep within the loving heart of a good God. You are seen without fault, because of what Jesus did.

So you are allowed to rest. You do not have to strive. You are already famous to God, and he is the one that counts. This is the truth. We muddle through life, but Jesus is the constant. He is on our side, and he is always inviting us to rest with him. That curious disquiet within us that we ignore – let it surface and bring it to Jesus. That conviction that we will never be good enough, even for ourselves – talk to Jesus about it today. Whatever pulls you away from knowing yourself beloved of God, don't let it disturb your rest any longer.

Read Numbers 6:24–26. May you feel God's smile today.

DI ARCHER

Breakfast with Jesus

When they got there, they found breakfast waiting for them – fish cooking over a charcoal fire, and some bread. 'Bring some of the fish you've just caught,' Jesus said. So Simon Peter went aboard and dragged the net to the shore… 'Now come and have some breakfast!' Jesus said. (NLT)

This is one of my favourite Bible stories. It is set in those confusing days after the crucifixion, when the disciples were trying to take in the fact that the man they saw suffocating to death on a cross was now very much alive. So, what did they do? They returned to the familiar to anchor themselves in this extraordinary new reality. They went fishing.

Seven of the disciples jumped in a boat and fished all night to no avail. Their skills seemed to have deserted them. But with the dawn came the suggestion from the figure on the shore that they throw the nets in a counter-intuitive way, on the other side of the boat, and then, of course, there were too many fish to deal with. No wonder that Peter recognised Jesus. He had done this before (Luke 5:4–6).

How kind of Jesus to meet them on their own terms and jog their memories, reassuring them that he was still the same Jesus they had loved and followed for the last three years. To cap it all, he had a traditional Galilean breakfast waiting for them when they landed. Surely those fish and breads must have rung a bell too.

Although we are searching for the spiritual roots of rest in God, never think that he separates them from the physical – nor, indeed, from the emotional or mental. The rest of God includes it all, for he made it all. He gave hungry, shocked men food before he began any deep conversations with them. Open your heart and hands and let him provide rest for you in all and any ways. Breakfast with Jesus on the lakeside was just what the disciples needed. Jesus does actually know what sort of rest you need too, even without you asking.

Dear Jesus, yes, you do know what I need. Please provide for me today and help me to recognise it when it comes. Amen

DI ARCHER

Rest beyond imagining

And the angel said to me, 'Write this: Blessed are those who are invited to the wedding feast of the Lamb.' And he added, 'These are true words that come from God.' (NLT)

We are on our way to the most amazing party we could ever imagine. Even if you are not a party girl, you will love this one. How do I know? Because the Bible says so here – everyone who goes to this party is 'blessed'. It will be the party to end all parties, beyond our imagination.

It will be part of the promised 'rest' that was instituted at creation and will find its fulfilment when Jesus wins, and we all celebrate. There will be rest from the incessant battle between God and evil, for Jesus, the faithful and true one (v. 11), will banish all the bad stuff forever. It just will not be allowed any more. It has no place in the kingdom of God. Only the good fruit of the Spirit will be there.

Jesus talked about the kingdom of heaven being like a feast. He wanted us to be part of it, and warned us against the distractions of the cares and charms of the day. He invited anyone who would respond, reaching out beyond the expected party guest list to include the hungry, the lame, the outcast, the foreigner and the needy. He included women, unlike his contemporary society, which regarded them as less valuable than men. He wants us all to be there. It is what he came for – to beckon us into his way of being, which actually works. Here and now. There and then.

Then, we will finally see the truth. We will know God's rest in ways we can only experience in part now. We will taste the wine of the kingdom. We will know as we are known. There is a seat with your name on it. He has reserved it for you.

Rest now. He has you in mind.

DI ARCHER

Abraham's journey of faith

Annie Willmot writes:

I did a tandem sky-dive once. After what felt like a very short safety briefing, I was whisked off towards the plane. It wasn't long before I was being strapped to my instructor as we edged towards the open plane door. In that moment, 13,000 feet up, I needed to have complete trust in my instructor as I literally put my life into his hands. Once I exited the plane and we accelerated towards the ground at 120 mph, I had to keep trusting that he would tell me when we'd reached 5,000 feet and it was time to deploy the parachute so we could land safely.

Having faith doesn't always require a literal leap. Every day we demonstrate faith: when we set our alarm before bed and expect it to wake us; when we sit down in a chair and have confidence that it won't fall apart; or when we turn our key in the door and expect it to open.

Having faith in God doesn't always feel so straightforward. Abraham's moment of great faith and obedience, when he is tested and asked to sacrifice his son, is one that is both challenging and awe-inspiring. However, what I find even more encouraging is Abraham's journey of faith to get to that moment. Abraham's story of faith is a hugely reassuring one. As Abraham learns to trust in God and to have faith in him, he falters and doubts. He fails many times, but he learns to trust in God's promises, and we see that God is always faithful.

Abraham's experiences help us to remember how God invites us to come as we are, completely imperfect and still learning every day, to walk alongside him. He is a faithful God, in spite of us.

Abraham's story is one that would take more than 14 days to study in full because it is the story of God's faithfulness, a narrative that goes on beyond Abraham's lifetime and has a huge and wonderful impact on our lives.

As we look at Abraham's journey of faith, let us pray that God would grow in us a strong faith and that we would learn to trust in him and his faithfulness more each day.

Stepping into the discomfort zone

The Lord had said to Abram, 'Leave your country, your people and your father's household and go to the land I will show you.' (NIV)

Armed with colourful pens and Post-It notes, in need of a job as I neared the end of university, I drew out all my options and I prayed. I told God, 'You can send me anywhere. But please don't send me to London.' I wanted to follow him wherever he would lead. I wanted to respond to his call. But I still wanted to be in control.

God found Abram living in a pagan land and he called Abram out of all that he had known. He told him to leave his country, his people and his family behind.

God's instruction to leave everything behind probably doesn't translate as well now, given the connected world we live in. We could move to the other side of the world and still pick up a phone and see someone's face moments after dialling their number.

God's instruction to Abram is more like God calling us to move to another planet without the possibility of connecting with the family we've left behind. In those days, extended family was a person's framework for security, their pension. God called Abram to leave behind all comfort and step into his discomfort zone.

In the end, God called me to London. It was certainly out of my comfort zone, but it wasn't a complete unknown like God's call for Abram. For Abram, his journey with God had already begun and this was the moment he stepped out into the complete unknown, so he could know God more. With each uncomfortable and unfamiliar step, he learned to put his faith in God and to depend on him.

Father God, help me when I am out of my comfort zone to choose to put my faith in you. Help me to learn to trust and depend on you. Amen

ANNIE WILLMOT

Making a name for yourself

'I will make your name great, and you will be a blessing.' (NIV)

When you die, what do you want to be remembered for? What will people think of when they hear your name? I have always loved the short mention Dorcas gets in Acts 9:36, where it says, 'She was always doing good and helping the poor.' What a wonderful way to be remembered. Or perhaps I'd like to be known for inventing something incredible, or for working on a project which impacted hundreds of people's lives.

In the Old Testament, the word 'name' also refers to reputation, fame or renown. At the Tower of Babel, we find men trying to make a name for themselves. They don't want to be known for doing good or helping the poor. They want to be known for themselves. They want to become like God. Seeing this, God confuses their language and scatters them across the earth.

In contrast, we find Abram, whose name means 'exalted father'. He came from an exalted family, but perhaps his name also infers how Abram would point to God as his heavenly Father. Abram was known because of his family, yet he wasn't seeking to make his name known, and God promises to make his name great, giving him the name Abraham, meaning 'father of many'.

God makes Abram's name great, but it was all in his timing and aligned with his calling, not for the sake of fame and pride. At the Tower of Babel people wanted to be seen. They wanted to be known. Sometimes we experience the same desire to be seen, to have our actions and hard work recognised. I wonder how things would look if our only desire was for God to be seen and for all our actions to glorify him and point to his great name.

Father, help me to focus on you today and to point others to your great name. Amen

ANNIE WILLMOT

What are you holding on to?

So Abram went, as the Lord had told him; and Lot went with him. (NIV)

Even if we're just popping to the shops, my four-year-old always makes sure he has all the essentials. His backpack will be bursting with cuddly toys, dinosaurs, snacks, a toy stethoscope, a spare hat and plenty of books. In one hand he'll be holding his toy pet carrier, complete with dog and veterinary tools, and in the other some kind of contraption made from copious amounts of masking tape, lollipop sticks and paper. It won't take long before he's feeling weighed down. Everything he's holding on to slows his progress and makes the journey difficult (for everyone!). Even so, encouraging him to part with any of his items can still be challenging.

Abram was told to leave behind his household, but his nephew Lot goes with him. It quickly becomes apparent that Lot doesn't share his uncle's vision. He doesn't get it. Abram is slowly developing his faith and learning to connect with God. Lot isn't. Tensions arise over wealth – they have too many possessions to share the same space – and Abram knows they need to separate. The separation is final – much like choosing to leave items at home can feel for a four-year-old! God invites us in Hebrews 12:1 to lay down the things that weigh us down, the things which stop us from following him and looking to Jesus.

It is hard to let go of things or people, to choose to follow God completely and wholeheartedly, without distraction. Over and over again we'll see Abram make hard choices as he chooses faith in God. As he does, God assures Abram of his promises for him, of his future. And we too are assured of a glorious inheritance.

Are you holding on to anything which is weighing you down? What would it look like to ask God to help you let go today?

ANNIE WILLMOT

Practising gratitude

**There he built an altar to the Lord and called on the name of the Lord.
(NIV)**

I'm not good at remembering to write in my journal. I love the idea of
journaling and I start with really good intentions, but a few weeks later,
I inevitably find my practically empty journal forgotten on my desk.
Recently, I wrote a piece titled 'I began journaling for a month, and here's
what I learned', which meant I actually had to make it a habit, at least
for a month.

As I wrote, I learned I needed to celebrate more, to practise being inten-
tionally thankful. In the busyness of life, I realised I overlooked things to be
thankful for and simply moved on to the next task. So, I challenged myself
to spend two minutes each day writing about things I was thankful for, and
to pause and thank God for those things. Some days, thankfulness flowed
on to the paper. Other days, writing was harder. However, each time, I felt
my heart shift into a place of praise and worship, focused on God.

Four times we find that Abram builds an altar. He practises gratitude.
He regularly pauses to worship God and to thank him for his promises,
provision and faithfulness. He connects with God, is obedient to him, and
ensures his focus is on him and all that he has done.

My journal entries are still pretty irregular; however, we do try to pause
and practise thankfulness in our home. At tea-time we ask, 'What was the
best bit of your day?' And we take it in turns to all thank God for something.
How do you pause and practise gratitude?

---

*Father, thank you for your faithfulness and provision. Help create in me a
thankful heart. Amen*

ANNIE WILLMOT

A sacred covenant

When the sun was down and it was dark, a smoking firepot and a flaming torch moved between the split carcasses. That's when God made a covenant with Abram. (MSG)

Shortly after we got engaged, my soon-to-be-husband got a nasty bout of tonsillitis. His tonsillitis wasn't going to kill him – although you might have thought so from the way he acted – however, while looking after him, I realised the enormity of the promises we would make when we got married. I would be choosing to enter into a partnership. I didn't know what the future might hold, but we were committing to love one another 'in sickness and in health… till death do us part'.

Abram, in conversation with God, asks how all that God promises is possible. In reply, God secures his promise with a covenant. It's like he upgrades a handshake to a contract.

Covenants involved slicing animals in half so both parties could walk between the pieces. A covenant was a commitment to partnership, a life-or-death agreement, like a marriage. But God's covenant with Abram was different because God made all the promises. Abram didn't have to fulfil any conditions in return. In fact, God sends Abram to sleep and gives him a vision for the future, and as he does, God passes through the pieces alone.

It's like he signs both sides of the covenant contract on Abram's behalf. He takes on the consequences if the covenant were to be broken and he makes an unconditional promise. He's not asking Abram to hold up some end of the deal. He's inviting Abram to partner with him and be part of his plans – plans which he promises will happen. God is always faithful, even if 'we are faithless, he will remain faithful' (2 Timothy 2:13, NIV).

Thank you, God, for your constant faithfulness. Help me to remember today that your faithfulness is not measured by my actions. Amen

ANNIE WILLMOT

Learning to be patient

'The Lord has kept me from having children.' (NIV)

My son hates traffic. As we slow at a red light, we hear his frustration from the back of the car. However, the satnav in our car has recently added symbols for upcoming traffic lights, which means he can watch and know when we are about to slow down. He likes to know the details and what to expect on a journey.

We live in an impatient, instant gratification culture. We can order things we want online to arrive next – or even the same – day, and then we can track the delivery, knowing exactly when our item might arrive. We like to know how things are going to happen and when we can expect them. But sometimes God doesn't give us all the information we think we need. He only tells us what he's going to do, not how he's going to do it.

Sarai's patience faltered because she didn't know how God's promises would be fulfilled. Rather than focusing on God and choosing to trust in his faithfulness, she focused on herself and on what had not yet happened. Struggling to believe how she would be able to have a son at her age, perhaps heartbroken that her body had not yet borne the son God had promised, Sarai found herself unable to keep waiting without knowing the details.

Patience looks like trusting in God and being okay with not knowing how his plans will come to fruition. It looks like choosing, over and over again, to believe in his faithfulness. Are there any parts of your life where you need to learn to wait more patiently for God to work?

Lord, help me to learn to be patient in prayer and give me strength to trust in your faithfulness, always. Amen

ANNIE WILLMOT

Taking matters into our own hands

'The Lord has kept me from having children. Go, sleep with my slave; perhaps I can build a family through her.' (NIV)

When we're having a conversation about a tricky situation, my husband and I have learned to check with each other, 'Do you want me to help fix it or just to listen?' Our innate response when we hear a problem is to try and find a solution. Even when we've agreed that I'm just listening, if I think I know the solution or what my husband is going to say, then I find keeping quiet a real challenge. I really struggle to sit with any kind of problem which I feel is unsolved. I like to keep talking and figuring it out until I have all the answers.

Virtually all of God's promises about Abram's future were dependent on him having a son, and Abram and Sarai saw it as a problem that it had not yet happened. They became impatient with waiting for God's promise and they took matters into their own hands. Sarai encouraged her husband Abram to sleep with her slave Hagar and she conceived.

Abram and Sarai's faith gave way to fear and, as they figured out their own solution, their focus moved from trusting God to concentrating on their circumstances, making decisions based on human reason and, ultimately, blaming one another when it didn't work out as they expected.

God, in his great love and mercy, turns the normal order upside down and keeps his covenant promise (while also caring for Hagar and her son) despite Abram and Sarai's 'problem-solving'.

Does your need to fix perceived problems or to figure out the details ever get in the way of you fully trusting in God?

God holds us in his hands, yet we decide to take matters into our own hands.
Pray: Father, I choose to open my hands, to lay it all down and trust fully in you today. Amen

ANNIE WILLMOT

What's in a name?

'No longer will you be called Abram; your name will be Abraham, for I have made you a father of many nations.' (NIV)

We all receive 'names' from the world. Growing up, my family encouraged my good academic results at school, and I was often labelled 'the clever one' of my siblings. I constantly strived to achieve grades worthy of the label I'd been given, and I felt a pressure to do well. I also took on labels which weren't encouraging, and I found myself worried that I was 'boring' long into early adulthood.

Perhaps you can think of labels which you have taken on. All of these names can become things we use to define ourselves, which we strive to constantly achieve or to avoid hearing again.

God re-names Abram. Abram means 'exalted father' and God changes his name to Abraham, meaning 'father of a great number'. God gives him a name which is yet another reflection of his promises for Abraham's life, inviting him to step into his identity as the father of many before Isaac is even born. He isn't giving him a label he needs to strive to achieve or live up to. Abraham's new name is symbolic of God's plans for his future, of all that God will do. He is inviting him, yet again, to place his confidence completely in God rather than in himself.

God has a new name for us (Revelation 2:17), a name which expresses our relationship with him, and his love and plans for us. God invites us to put down the labels and to find the core of our confidence in him. Like Abraham, we can delight in our incompleteness, knowing that we have a future because God is faithful.

Father God, remind me today of your goodness and faithfulness as I put down the labels I have taken from the world and focus on your promises for me. Amen

ANNIE WILLMOT

Disconnection and disbelief

Abraham and Sarah were old by this time, very old. Sarah was far past the age for having babies. Sarah laughed within herself. 'An old woman like me? Get pregnant? With this old man of a husband?' (MSG)

I remember attending a summer Christian festival as a teenager. It was ministry time in the big tent, and I was standing among thousands of young people. Everyone else seemed to be connecting with God, but I wasn't. The meeting leader was encouraging people to share what God was saying to them and there were all these stories of how God was speaking to each person about his plans for their future. In that moment, I felt disconnected from God and I struggled to believe that he had plans for me.

Abraham wrestled with doubt even though he regularly chatted to God, so it's perhaps not surprising that Sarah, who didn't seem to have the same close, personal relationship or journey with God, might struggle to believe she was really going to have a baby. She is now old and when she's told it will happen next year, she doesn't believe it. She laughs.

God's promise was given to Abraham and I wonder if, even though she was to be mother to this promised son, she felt on the outside of this promise. We see in this passage her disconnection and disbelief. I would love to have been a fly on the wall during Abraham and Sarah's conversations over the years. Do they still talk and wonder whether they really will have a child? Has Sarah become despondent and convinced it's never really going to happen?

Do you sometimes feel disconnected or struggle to believe that God's promises are for *you*? In Sarah's hopelessness, God reminds her that nothing is impossible for him and then he even names their son Isaac, meaning 'one laughs' – a reminder that he brings laughter and joy out of the seemingly impossible!

Thank you, God, that all things are possible for you. Help me to know joy, laughter and connection with you today. Amen

ANNIE WILLMOT

Honest conversation

It's impossible to please God apart from faith. And why? Because anyone who wants to approach God must believe both that he exists *and* that he cares enough to respond to those who seek him. (MSG)

At a prayer meeting many years ago, a friend who had recently joined our church turned to me and said, 'I can't talk to God today because I'm angry at him.' She believed she could only go to God when she felt thankful or happy. We reflected a lot on how God invites us into relationship. He's not a distant God sat up high on a cloud somewhere, making decisions about our lives with no way for us to connect with him. He doesn't invite us into the kind of relationship where we have to pretend to be okay. He invites us into a two-way, open and honest relationship where we can pour out our deepest, darkest emotions and he loves us no less. God welcomes our doubts and fears because he welcomes us – every last bit of us.

Abraham approaches God with boldness and is met with conversation. God invites him to speak to him as a friend, evoking his questions. God welcomes us to bring before him our fears, insecurities and even to share when we have objections to what he seems to be doing.

Abraham's prayers are built upon his faith in God. He didn't silently accept God's word; he engaged with it. He had faith to be bold and persistent, and to plead for those who needed God's mercy and grace. God invites us to do the same as we seek him. Have you ever pleaded with God in prayer with the same intensity and compassion shown by Abraham? I'm not sure I ever have. What would it look like if you were to come before God today, totally open and honest, sharing everything that is on your heart?

Thank God that he invites us to approach him boldly. Think of someone in your life who desperately needs God's mercy and grace. Pray for them this week in the same way Abraham prayed for Sodom and Gomorrah.

ANNIE WILLMOT

Good things take time

Now the Lord was gracious to Sarah as he had said, and the Lord did for Sarah what he had promised. Sarah became pregnant and bore a son to Abraham in his old age, at the very time God had promised him. (NIV)

American basketball coach John Wooden said, 'Good things take time, as they should. We shouldn't expect good things to happen overnight. Actually, getting something too easily or too soon can cheapen the outcome.'

Lots of good things take time. Cheddar cheese, for example, is aged through a process called Cheddaring, where the blocks of curd are stacked on top of one another in order to squeeze the additional liquid, the whey, out of the one below. And that's just a part of a process which can take two to three months or, for the oldest Cheddar, up to ten years. There is a lot of waiting in the process.

Over 20 years had passed since God first promised Abraham a son, and throughout that time God had been shaping, moulding and maturing Abraham's character. The waiting has been important, and God's timing was precise.

Like he was in Abraham, God is at work in us (Philippians 1:6). Character and faith don't appear overnight. As we wait for God's promises, he develops our faith and endurance. God knows we will stumble and fail along the way, yet he remains faithful. Reading stories like this of God's faithfulness and his fulfilment of his promises encourages us to persevere.

If God had given Abraham and Sarah a son sooner, would Abraham's faith and character have developed so strongly? If Sarah had Isaac before she was an old woman, would they have proclaimed that through God all things are possible? When we are in the midst of the waiting, it can be hard to imagine the outcome, and hard to know that we are experiencing personal and spiritual growth; but God's timing is precise and he is at work.

Father God, help me to seek you daily and to trust that you are shaping and moulding my character to be more like you as I connect with you. Amen

ANNIE WILLMOT

Abraham was tested

He said, 'Take your dear son Isaac whom you love and go to the land of Moriah. Sacrifice him there as a burnt offering on one of the mountains that I'll point out to you.' (MSG)

When I was taking my A-levels, all of my exams got scheduled on the same day. Since it wasn't physically possible to take more than one exam at the same time, some were re-scheduled to the next day and I had to be kept in isolation so there was no conferring with friends who had already taken the exam.

The problem with overnight isolation is that you can't do it in an empty classroom at school. I had my phone confiscated and I had to stay at a teacher's house. As an awkward teenager who was already nervous about exams, the whole experience was pretty uncomfortable. However, although it was a hard test to face, at least I had prepared myself for the exams and knew roughly what to expect when it came to the test itself.

Abraham faces an incredibly difficult test but, unlike my exams, he hadn't had the opportunity to revise his answers in advance.

We've followed Abraham's rocky journey of faith as he questions God and asks for reassurance along the way. However, in this moment his response is immediate and unquestioning obedience. We read nothing of Abraham's internal struggles. We know he loves his son, but still he faithfully obeys God. Abraham's faith journey *has* been revision for this moment, he just didn't know it.

Abraham is certain that God keeps his promises and God is always good. He trusts him fully and he demonstrates that he loves God more than anything or anyone else; more than his son, his future, his own happiness. He is willing to lay down and sacrifice his precious son, knowing God is powerful enough to raise him from the dead (Hebrews 11:19). His faith is tested and it stands strong.

What part of your life would you struggle to lay down and sacrifice? Ask God to grow in you a strong faith like Abraham.

ANNIE WILLMOT

Stories of faith and obedience

All these people were still living by faith when they died. They did not receive the things promised; they only saw them and welcomed them from a distance (NIV)

Stories of great faith are inspiring. My granny thought nothing of staying up all night to pray if something was on her heart, and she served her church and community faithfully. She had a quiet, unassuming and powerful faith in God.

Hudson Taylor was a man whose life was characterised by incredible faith. His unswerving belief in God's faithfulness and his perseverance in prayer led to many lives being changed in China and beyond.

Corrie ten Boom's faith inspired her to offer shelter, food and protection to those in need, including saving the lives of some 800 Jews during the Holocaust in World War II.

In the Bible, Noah built the ark and saved his family. Joshua attacked Jericho and saw the walls come down. Abraham obeyed and saw God's promises fulfilled, and even Isaac, who would have been old enough to put up a fight, climbed upon the altar. He had seen his father's faith, and he demonstrates great faith too. Then, of course, we see Jesus' obedience to the point of death on the cross, which led to our forgiveness.

In our family we love sharing stories of people who have trusted in God, from those who were quietly faithful, to those who trusted in the God of the impossible and saw life-changing things happen. In fact, we even named our son after Hudson Taylor!

Faith and obedience enable us to draw nearer to God and to trust him whatever our circumstances. And, like Abraham with Isaac, our faith can encourage others too. We can encourage our children, grandchildren, friends and family into relationship with a faithful God. Who in your life encourages you to go deeper in your faith? Do you recognise God's faithfulness at work in your own life?

Read a story today of someone whose life was characterised by their faith in God and, as you do, pray that God would use their story to strengthen your faith.

ANNIE WILLMOT

Our journey isn't finished yet

Those who have faith are children of Abraham. Scripture foresaw that God would justify the Gentiles by faith, and announced the gospel in advance to Abraham: 'All nations will be blessed through you.' So those who rely on faith are blessed along with Abraham, the man of faith. (NIV)

Not long after we had our first baby, my husband and I both felt God call us to leave our jobs. Not knowing what was next, many people questioned why we didn't wait until we'd figured out the next step, but we felt certain God was asking us to step out and have faith. Now we look back on that step and all that followed, and see it as a significant moment in our own stories of faith. Each of us has our own story, our own faith journey, and we're not finished yet.

Abraham has had many pivotal and formative moments in his faith journey so far, but this isn't where his story finishes. And Abraham's story also has wonderful implications for us. God's covenant promise was fulfilled through Jesus, a descendant of Abraham. Because of Abraham, *we* are blessed.

In his letter to the Galatians, Paul shares how God's blessings for us are far greater than land, possessions or descendants. The ultimate, incredible blessing we are promised is God's Holy Spirit to live within us. God invites us into a new covenant, a new partnership, initiated by him, through Jesus on the cross. He offers us forgiveness and he invites us into relationship.

God doesn't expect perfection. Like Abraham who faltered, doubted and asked questions along the way, God invites us to come as we are. As we draw close to him, we learn to trust him and our faith continues to grow.

Abraham demonstrated how it can take a lifetime to build a deep faith. What have you learned from Abraham's journey? What is the next step in your own journey of faith going to look like?

Father God, thank you for your promises. Thank you that you invite us into relationship and that you are always faithful. Amen

ANNIE WILLMOT

Jesus' sacrifice for us (Hebrews 8—10)

Lakshmi Jeffreys writes:

Holy Week, the seven days beginning with Palm Sunday, is one of the most dramatic in the Bible. Many churches mark the events of Jesus' last days on earth with processions, meals or prayer nights and so on.

Exploring the meaning of Jesus' sacrifice from Hebrews initially seems an odd choice for Holy Week. For a start, many years ago I remember people looking for the letter to the Hebrews in the Old Testament. It is an understandable error when so much of the letter concerns the temple, blood, priests and facets of worship familiar to Jewish people in the years before and immediately after Jesus, but unknown to most of us.

Yet the drama of the days leading to Jesus' crucifixion and the visceral description of worship in the temple are in tune with each other. The unknown author was writing to people who were once devout and sincere followers of Jewish traditions in their quest to be God's people. Somehow these Jews discovered that Jesus Christ is the promised Messiah, and they formed a church. Now they were struggling.

Once used to prescribed worship involving robed male priests sacrificing animals on an altar, they needed to discover why such rituals were no longer necessary. Even worse, they were persecuted for abandoning their former practices. Where was God?

This question still confronts Christians. I love Holy Week traditions. Your expression of faith might rely more on songs, a special place, particular groups of people with whom you pray and study the Bible, liturgy, types of church leader – you will know. There is nothing wrong with any of these until we notice how uncomfortable we become when something changes. Meanwhile, Christians who are persecuted for their faith are more than uncomfortable. In all cases we need to remember Jesus' sacrifice on the cross, which transformed everything, and the Holy Spirit who will transform us.

I am indebted to Bishop Donald Allister, who allowed me to use material he prepared for a Lent course on Hebrews broadcast in 2021. I invite you to read not just chapters 8—10, but the whole letter. Then be prepared for theology, covenants, lots of blood, personal discomfort and, I pray, a renewing of your mind and heart.

Palm Sunday – expectancy vs expectations

Here is the main point: We have a High Priest who sat down in the place of honour beside the throne of the majestic God in heaven. (NLT)

The Hebrews were steeped in tradition and understanding of the Messiah, the promised Saviour. Somehow, they had equated this person with Jesus. Now that they were following him, everything should have been put right – God's rule should have been restored. Instead, they were being persecuted and had no priests to make sacrifices for their sins. What had happened?

The Hebrews knew that Aaron had been appointed the first high priest in the wilderness with Moses and God's people, when God established forms of worship familiar to the Hebrews. So, in chapter 7, the author reminded them of the story in Genesis 14:18–24. King Melchizedek of Salem (which eventually became Jerusalem) was a 'priest of God Most High' and blessed Abraham, the 'father' of God's people. In other words, centuries before the law of Moses, God blessed Abraham through a high priest. Jesus was now the true high priest and king, like Melchizedek, not Aaron. God's rule was restored, but not as the Hebrews imagined.

Today is Palm Sunday and Christians across the globe will recall Jesus' triumphal entry into Jerusalem on a donkey. Perhaps the Hebrews had heard about Jesus behaving exactly as the prophets foretold. The crowds went wild, hailing Jesus as king. Here was the promised Messiah, who would save them from the Romans. When Jesus did not behave as the crowd expected, they called for his death. Might the Hebrews make a connection with their expectations?

It is worth reflecting on what we expect from Jesus. Consider the difference between expecting and expectations. We expect God to act, but the problem arises when we decide what that action should be. What do you do when God does not meet your expectations?

Loving God, challenge my expectations. Show me who you really are and how to become the person you call me to be. Amen

LAKSHMI JEFFREYS

Holy Monday – the danger of falling back into old ways

When God speaks of a 'new' covenant, it means he has made the first one obsolete. It is now out of date and will soon disappear. (NLT)

Jesus came to fulfil the purpose of the laws made between God and Moses. Perhaps today we would say Jesus 'signed off' the law. In fact, the Old Testament law encompassed three strands: moral law, for example the ten commandments, told people how to live. Jesus referred to this in the sermon on the mount. Today, systems of justice across the world uphold commands not to kill or steal. Civil law, on the other hand, applied only to God's people in the Old Testament, who were surrounded by hostile nations. Jesus transformed thinking about these, and while modern societies follow several principles, this is not in the way they were enshrined. Finally comes ceremonial law, involving priesthood and sacrifice. This was superseded when Jesus died on the cross.

In Old Testament worship, the blood of animals was offered by the high priest to forgive people for their sins. This was to symbolise restored relationship with God, a picture of what happened if people kept the law. But this image did not stop people from breaking the law. When Jesus offered himself as a perfect sacrifice, his blood was accepted by God, and the Holy Spirit came to write God's law in the minds and on the hearts of God's people. Jesus' death ended the need for symbolic rituals and rules. Transformed minds, hearts and lives were available to everyone.

Interestingly, many of us prefer rules to relationship. We want God to change our circumstances, or we blame ourselves for falling short of the law. In either case, God is at a distance and we need not change. Jesus' sacrifice on the cross offers intimacy with God where transformation is inevitable. This is both wonderful and terrifying. We need regular prayer and encouragement not to return to what feels comfortable.

After one person regularly prayed, 'Lord, sweep the cobwebs from my heart, my mind, my life', an exasperated member of the group prayed for transformation: 'Lord, kill the spider!'

LAKSHMI JEFFREYS

Holy Tuesday – perfectly clean

Just think how much more the blood of Christ will purify our consciences from sinful deeds so that we can worship the living God. For by the power of the eternal Spirit, Christ offered himself to God as a perfect sacrifice for our sins. (NLT)

A couple of years ago, I discovered I had deeply hurt someone on several occasions, each time unintentionally. When I realised what I had done, I felt dreadful.

In Jesus' day, the temple was symbolic of the true 'tabernacle' in heaven. As mentioned yesterday, the purpose of sacrifice was to offer a picture of what was required to be put right with God. There were certain sacrifices for sins people knew they had committed, and provision made for people like me, who had sinned without realising. Once a year the high priest would 'sweep up' all the sins which had not been atoned for in other worship, first offering a sacrifice for his own sins. This took place in the 'most holy place', vividly described in the letter.

Of course, the cleansing from sin was merely ceremonial. No lasting change would take place in anyone. You might remember Jesus' words about the religious leaders who appeared pure on the outside but were hypocrites, like whitewashed tombs (Matthew 23:27). They went through outward rituals but remained sinful. Once Jesus had died on the cross, however, there was no longer the requirement for a building and ceremonial washing in blood. His blood was accepted by God in heaven once for all. There was no more external washing; instead, our consciences could be cleansed by the Holy Spirit.

As soon as I discovered my sin, I could repent – turn towards Jesus, away from self-loathing (and occasional self-righteousness) – and confess what I had done, before receiving God's forgiveness. Whenever I sin, I can remember Jesus' sacrifice for my sin and return directly to God who will cleanse me from inside by the Holy Spirit.

When Jesus had finished washing the disciples' feet, he declared all the disciples were clean – except Judas. Love of money stopped Judas being fully clean. Ask Jesus to cleanse you from whatever soils your heart or conscience.

LAKSHMI JEFFREYS

Holy Wednesday – the inheritance

Christ offered himself to God as a perfect sacrifice for our sins. That is why he is the one who mediates a new covenant between God and people, so that all who are called can receive the eternal inheritance God has promised them. (NLT)

When my parents died, their wills came into effect and, after probate, my siblings and I came into our inheritance. Until they died the will was an important legal document, but it had no power of itself to change our lives. The writer to the Hebrews uses this analogy for the old covenant. In fact, covenant, testament and will are interchangeable in this context. Jesus is the author of the covenant, as my parents wrote their wills. Once Jesus died, the will – the new covenant, new testament – came into effect: we could inherit eternal salvation by the Holy Spirit.

The old covenant was sealed in worship by the blood of an animal, sacrificially killed. This death symbolised the change in status between people and God, but the change was temporary and the sacrifice had to be repeated. The new covenant was sealed in Jesus' blood – the sacrifice was complete. The one who died brought us into perfect relationship with God, once and for all. Jesus' blood, not that of a bull or goat, gave us access to God for all time.

The writer to the Hebrews talked about salvation not simply from sin. Persecution was rife and the new Christians needed the assurance that Jesus would come to save them in full. Because of Jesus' death, they were right with God already – their sins had been forgiven. They could look to Jesus for comfort and hope in their troubles. He had died for them and they would be reminded that he interceded for them in heaven. They could trust him.

I am reminded of Jesus' prayer for his disciples in the garden of Gethsemane. He prayed that they would not be removed from the world but would remain safe and holy in the truth.

Pray for Christians around the world enduring persecution. May God protect them from the evil one.

LAKSHMI JEFFREYS

Maundy Thursday – true worship

The old system under the law of Moses was only a shadow, a dim preview of the good things to come, not the good things themselves. The sacrifices under that system were repeated again and again, year after year, but they were never able to provide perfect cleansing for those who came to worship. (NLT)

Maundy Thursday is commemorated in different ways. Some church leaders ceremonially wash the feet of other people in their church during or after a special service of Holy Communion. You might be familiar with 'agape' meals, Passover suppers or services of prayer into the night. It is important to remember Jesus' last meal with his friends, how he demonstrated humble service, and his prayers of agony in the garden of Gethsemane before his arrest. The difficulty comes when the ritual or act of remembering becomes more important than spending time with Jesus as we are and allowing the Holy Spirit to transform us.

One of the most shocking verses to orthodox Jews in the whole letter is Hebrews 10:4, where the writer spells out that it is impossible for the blood of bulls and goats to take away sins. The whole religious structure did not work! Instead, Jesus came to abolish the law and systems of worship established by the law. He replaced it by doing God's will and enabling believers to live in God's will. There are no special actions, places, rituals or anything else necessary to enable us to be in God's presence.

It is hard for the modern reader to understand the full force of these words. Yet we also can become fixated on outward signs, sacraments, music, sermons, buildings or even people. Without these we might consider the worship is not proper; we feel we cannot meet God. The constant message of Hebrews is that outward expressions do not get us right with God. These are merely signs of an inward reality. What makes the difference is the blood of Jesus, offered in heaven for all sins, for all time. Our task is to enjoy God and learn to live in God's will alongside one another.

What makes church or a Christian gathering 'right' for you? Thank God for particular people, places or activities that enable you to worship and pray they do not become idols.

LAKSHMI JEFFREYS

Good Friday – access to God

By his death, Jesus opened a new and life-giving way through the curtain into the Most Holy Place. And since we have a great High Priest who rules over God's house, let us go right into the presence of God with sincere hearts fully trusting him. (NLT)

Today I invite you to read through the account of Jesus' crucifixion from any or all of the Gospels. Matthew 27 and Mark 15 describe how the curtain of the temple was torn from top to bottom. In Luke 23 Jesus speaks words of forgiveness from the cross, and in John 19 Jesus says, 'It is finished.'

Just as the priest would have sprinkled the blood of animals over the worshippers to offer a picture of being forgiven by God, so now Christians are sprinkled with Jesus' blood. Jesus' work is complete. There is no longer a sanctuary, the domain of male priests. Christians are all priests in God's eyes – the priesthood of all believers – because, by the blood of Jesus, we can all enter the most holy place and be directly in the presence of God. Jesus is the mediator between us and God.

Most of us know the theory of Jesus' death on the cross allowing us to approach God with confidence and full assurance of faith. Many, however, still seek another mediator. There appears to be an innate need for someone holier, a 'better Christian than I am'. So many able, gifted Christian women I know do not feel good enough for anything, including approaching God.

It is wonderful to ask for the prayers of other people. Indeed, tomorrow we shall explore the need to be alongside other Christian believers. At the same time, it is essential to remember that we have full, glorious access to the creator of everything because of Jesus' death. The only barriers to God's presence are those we put in ourselves. And surely to do so is to deny Jesus' sacrifice for us.

Knowing that Jesus has opened the way, spend time today with God, however tentative you might feel, and allow your thoughts and emotions to surface. Ask God to remove any barriers you have erected.

LAKSHMI JEFFREYS

Holy Saturday – love

So do not throw away this confident trust in the Lord. Remember the great reward it brings you! Patient endurance is what you need now, so that you will continue to do God's will. Then you will receive all that he has promised. (NLT)

Wherever in the world you were in 2020, you will have experienced lockdown. Holy Saturday, often empty and desolate in feel, reminds me of that year when seeing others was through an electronic device or on a walk, a metre or two apart. Nothing was as it should have been.

Many people began to question why they went to church. It is important to be reminded of Jesus' death on the cross for our sins. Yet, whether or not we are at church, our sins remain forgiven. Many people like to receive Holy Communion, bread and wine, broken and given, but Christ's body remains broken and his blood given, regardless of our participation in a service. We like to meet God to pray and sing alongside others, but that is primarily for our benefit.

Perhaps the most important aspect of church, according to Hebrews, was not allowed during lockdown: this is to eat, drink and chat together, with Jesus in our midst. There is something unique about mixing with people, some of whom are the same as us and others different from us – when we do this in the name of Jesus.

The letter to the Hebrews teaches that love is encouraging others to do good deeds. This makes gathering with other Christians an act of obedience to God. If we choose not to meet people in the name of Jesus, we discourage, rather than encourage others, and therefore disobey.

Hebrews also suggests we go to church so that we do not fall away. If we have known God and been together with others, then to neglect God and other people is a fearful thing. More positively, we support others or are supported through hardship and persecution with faith, hope and love as we remember what Jesus has done for us.

Take some time to reflect on what Jesus' sacrifice on the cross means for you, personally and then for your church. Then tomorrow's celebrations will be even more poignant.

LAKSHMI JEFFREYS

Jesus' promise: 'I am with you always'

Sandra Wheatley writes:

In the opening chapter of Matthew's gospel he includes a reference from Isaiah 7:14, 'The virgin will... give birth to a son, and they will call him Immanuel (which means, "God with us").' Even before he was born, Jesus was called 'God with us'.

Sometimes the word 'Emmanuel' (an alternative spelling) is relegated to Christmastime and is forgotten the rest of the year. But this name, this title, this truth is something to cherish and meditate upon every day. I love it! During the next two weeks, I'm hoping we can explore the reality of the abiding presence of Jesus in our lives, our Emmanuel with us 24/7, as we study his encounters with ordinary people in the gospels.

In the final verse of Matthew's gospel, Jesus gives the disciples 'the great commission' and within it 'the great promise' – he will be with us always and in *all* ways! Jesus gave a promise he has never failed to keep. He is the greatest promise-giver and promise-keeper.

Of all the things Jesus could have promised the disciples – and us – I wonder why it was this promise to be with us that supersedes all the others he gave. Is it that our God is a relational God, and throughout his life here Jesus knew just how important it was, and would be, that the disciples were with him – and he with them in every situation they faced?

Jesus knew what it was to feel abandoned, to be alone in the darkest of times. He knows. And perhaps that is why his promise is so vital to us.

During my time at a very remote mission station in the depths of the African bush, I was left entirely alone for days. The mission station had been under attack for a week or more by members of a neighbouring tribe who wanted control of it. The missionaries I lived with decided they could no longer stay. I was left alone to run the small maternity unit, the orphanage and the daily clinic. I knew I had to stay.

On the first night of my 'abandonment' I read Jesus' words from John's gospel, 'Yet I am not alone, for my Father is with me' (John 16:32, NIV). I knew Jesus understood exactly how terrified I was but, 'like-Father-like-Son', his promise to be with me was true. Over 40 years later, it still is.

It started with a promise...

'He is not here; he has risen, just as he said.' (NIV)

It may seem a little contradictory to begin to explore Jesus' promise to be with us always with 'he is not here'! But on this Easter Day, I couldn't resist looking at Mary's encounter with Jesus at the tomb, because she experienced that sense of loss and separation from Jesus that none of us will ever know – yet sometimes feel as if we do. I also want to remind us that Jesus had made a promise – and he kept it. Many times Jesus told his disciples that he would die and would rise again. It was a promise that Mary and the disciples had forgotten.

Mary Magdalene and Mary, the mother of Jesus, were the last ones to leave the cross and the first to go to the tomb on Easter morning. We can only imagine the depth of their sorrow and sense of loss as they approached the tomb, and their shock at what greeted them – an angel sitting on the stone that had once sealed Jesus' tomb.

The angel who rolled back the stone didn't open the tomb to let Jesus out. The tomb was opened to let the women see inside!

Yet it wasn't until Mary's encounter with Jesus, who she mistook for the gardener, that the promise became a reality as Jesus spoke her name (John 20:16).

Easter Day brings such hope, and the sure and certain assurance that Jesus' words to us – those special, significant promises he has given to you and to me – will be kept, 'just as he said'.

'Christ is risen, he is risen indeed.' Lord Jesus, my risen and ever-present Saviour, I worship you today. Amen

SANDRA WHEATLEY

His call

He appointed twelve that they might be with him. (NIV)

When I was 14 years old, I was convinced God was calling me to be a missionary. Whether I was more influenced by the film *The Nun's Story* with Audrey Hepburn, rather than an audible 'call' from God, wasn't totally clear! But during the first day of my student nurse training in the 1970s, when asked why I wanted to be a nurse, my response sealed my fate as the resident religious crank – 'I'm going to be a missionary to Africa,' I declared! Four years later, I was on my way to a mission station in a very remote part of south-west Kenya. I loved every moment of my time there.

Some 40 years later, I've learned so much more about the 'call' of God. When Jesus called the disciples, the primary reason was 'to be with him'. He called them into a relationship with him – the *being* before any *doing*. And the same is still true today. Each of us is called: it isn't just the talented, the anointed, the academic, the charismatic.

It is you and me: mums, daughters, sisters, aunties, grandmas; the washer-uppers, the nappy-changers, the child-minders, the carers; those who pray, the givers of time, the listeners, the encouragers… His call includes everyone, and it is a relationship that is reciprocal because his promise to us is to be with us always. What is ours to him?

For half of my adult life I have lived within the constraints of MS. Immobility and inability mean my days of doing are long gone. And yet Jesus' call resonates in my heart. Nothing can or ever will separate me from him. From my days in the depths of the African bush to the confines of my wheelchair, he is with me… always.

Father God, in the midst of all we face today, let us hear your call as it resonates in our hearts. Be with us, Lord. Amen

SANDRA WHEATLEY

In the storms

One day Jesus said to his disciples, 'Let's go over to the other side of the lake.' So they got into a boat and set out. (NIV)

The moment we commit ourselves to Jesus and ask him into our lives, he takes us at our word! The disciples had no way of knowing what was about to happen when they clambered into the boat. They were simply on their way with Jesus 'to the other side'. He has entered into these 'little boats' of ours too and has said those same words to us: 'Let's go.'

I recall that day when I started my journey with him, trusting that he knew where we were going and how we would get there. Conscious of his presence with me guarding and guiding, I knew I was safe with him.

As they journeyed across the lake a storm arose, which wasn't uncommon, but such was its severity that the disciples, some experienced fishermen, feared for their lives. As they looked to Jesus, they discovered he was asleep. Asleep in a storm!

How many times has this situation been ours? Storms come in many guises, don't they? It sometimes feels like these tiny boats of ours cannot possibly keep us safe as we're tossed around.

Not long after I set sail with Jesus, things got a little bumpy, and 'abundant life' suddenly looked very much like an imminent death! I quickly realised that rather than looking at the storm, I should look to Jesus. I did – he looked as if he was taking a nap! And yet his presence with me was evidence of the promise he made me – 'I am with you, always.' Without fail, through every storm this life brings, his promise still stands. Even today.

If a deluge looks as if it will overwhelm you and you feel that Jesus is taking a nap, remind yourself of his promise to you… it is yours.

Dear Lord, be to me the God of the journey and not just of the destination. Remind me that as you were with me in the past, so you are with me now and always. Amen

SANDRA WHEATLEY

In the waiting times

When Jesus saw him lying there and learned that he had been in this condition for a long time, he asked him, 'Do you want to get well?' (NIV)

Some are born to wait; others have waiting thrust upon them; and then there are those who achieve the ability to wait simply because there is little else that they can do.

Today I found myself consciously waiting. As I lay on my bed gazing out across my garden, I was so aware of waiting with God. Not for him, but *with* him. The man lying at the pool had been waiting for 38 years, longing for the waters to stir and his chance to be the first in to be healed. Thirty-eight years – that's longer than Jesus had been alive!

Of all those waiting around that pool, Jesus saw this man, drew alongside him and healed him.

Sickness affects us all – righteous and unrighteous, saint and sinner – we're all susceptible to illness, infection and accidents. Long-term illness, pain or disability can all make us feel isolated and alone. And sometimes we wonder, 'Where is Jesus?'

When I was diagnosed with MS, Jesus said, 'I am with you, always.' As the disease progressed and I lost my job, my home and many of my friends, Jesus said, 'I am with you, always.' When I could no longer walk as I once did, could no longer sit up or move without excruciating pain, Jesus said, 'I am with you, always.'

My longing and waiting for healing continues to this day. So, like the man at the Pool of Bethesda, I wait with him and know he will take this body of mine and hold it. Healing is in his time, in his hands. There is a sense of wholeness as I realise again that his presence *is* the evidence of his promise.

Father God, for those called to 'wait', help us to know it is your presence that brings wholeness and healing. We place our hope and trust in you, always. Amen

SANDRA WHEATLEY

In our caring

'Truly I tell you, whatever you did for one of the least of these brothers and sisters of mine, you did for me.' (NIV)

I still remember my first day on the wards as a student nurse. In the midst of the busyness and feeling totally overwhelmed by the world I had stepped into, I helped a very ill woman to have a drink. As I held the glass to her lips, she cupped her hands over mine and smiled as she drank. Jesus' words suddenly became real to me. What I was doing for her, I was doing for him. From that moment I realised what my nursing career was all about – seeing him in everyone I cared for.

Caring and kindness come in many forms, as Jesus outlines in verses 35–36. The incredible thing is that we still have those same opportunities today: giving food to the hungry, hospitality to the homeless, reaching out to those in prison and seeing him in each person we encounter.

There are an estimated 13.6 million carers in the UK (2020 figures), 59% of whom are women. You may be one of those women. You know the emotional and physical cost of caring. You know it goes way beyond a gesture of kindness – it is a commitment that can last for years. Meanwhile, your life is on hold and you may feel isolated and utterly alone as you ensure your loved one is safe, comfortable and living a life of worth and quality.

Whether caring for someone with a physical impairment or seeing them fade into the horrors of dementia or Alzheimer's, is it still possible to know that Jesus is where he said he would be? With us? As we see him in the one we care for or when we're literally on our knees with exhaustion and despair, can we hear him say, 'I am with you, always, even here, even now'? Yes, we can!

Dear Father, you are the God who sees me and us (Genesis 16:13). Even in the lonely, isolated places of caring for others, even there you are with us. Thank you. Amen

SANDRA WHEATLEY

Out on a limb

He wanted to see who Jesus was … So he ran ahead and climbed a sycamore tree. (NIV)

'There must be more than this' – do you remember this worship song? Sometimes the winds of change rustle our settled and safe lives, and we wonder and long for something more.

The story of Zacchaeus' encounter with Jesus perhaps illustrates this. He was a wealthy man living in Jericho. He collected Roman taxes from his fellow Jews and probably added to his income by charging over and above what the Romans demanded. He was hated and despised.

But he was also curious; curious about a man called Jesus who he'd heard would be passing through Jericho that day. Was Zacchaeus wondering if there was more to life than wealth and possessions? As he was small in stature, he decided to climb a tree to get a better view of Jesus.

Then the remarkable encounter takes place – Jesus not only sees him in the tree, but also calls him by his name! There are only a handful of people in Luke's gospel who Jesus calls by name – Zacchaeus is one of them. And then Jesus invites himself to his house, the only time in the gospels where this happened. This despised sinner was to have Jesus as a guest in his house.

The transformation in Zacchaeus was incredible – instead of the passion to *get*, he now had a passion to *give* (v. 8).

Zacchaeus did not know that when Jesus passed through Jericho that day, he was going to Jerusalem for the last time. Had Zacchaeus procrastinated, his opportunity to meet with Jesus would have gone.

Jesus knew he would be in the tree. He called him by his name and transformed his life. Jesus said he had come 'to seek and to save what was lost' (v. 10) and that is exactly what he did, and still does.

Jesus is still passing our way. When we're feeling lost, out on a limb or wondering about change, he sees us where we are and calls us by our name. And his promise once again rings true: 'I am with you, always.'

SANDRA WHEATLEY

In the midst of loss

When the Lord saw her, his heart went out to her and he said, 'Don't cry.' (NIV)

This is the only mention of Nain and this widow's story in scripture. Jesus arrived in Nain from Capernaum accompanied by a huge crowd. As they come to the town gate, a much more subdued crowd are leaving. At the head of that crowd is a widow and behind her the funeral bier carrying her only son. Two only-sons meet, one alive and destined to die, the other dead but destined to live.

There are no words from the widow, no pleas for Jesus' help or falling at his feet begging for healing. There is nothing she could say. Her only son was dead. She may not have known anything about Jesus, but Jesus was there, and his heart went out to her. He was moved to the core of his being. He touched the coffin, spoke to the young man and raised him back to life, then gave him back to his mum. No requests were made for him to do anything, he just did it.

Then the people said, 'God has come to help his people.' Does that sound familiar? 'God with us… Emmanuel.'

Unlike many other instances of Jesus' healings and miracles in scripture, faith is never mentioned in this story. Jesus had simply appeared and had compassion on the woman. That changed everything.

Perhaps today, for you in your particular 'Nain', you need to know that Jesus is with you too. Whether for you it is the actual loss of a loved one or the death of a dream, career or relationship; if you feel you have no more strength to plead for help or that your faith is in tatters, know that Jesus is there, he has come to help you today.

Lord, sometimes we have no words, yet you know what to do. Death in whatever shape or form it comes is no match for you. Please help us, Lord. Amen

SANDRA WHEATLEY

In the wilderness

Then Jesus was led by the Spirit into the wilderness to be tempted by the devil. (NIV)

The story of Jesus' time in the wilderness and the temptations he faced are perhaps familiar to us all – especially during Lent.

But it is the 'wilderness' that I'd like us to focus on today, as it was in the wilderness that Jesus' ministry began, not in a blaze of publicity in full view of everyone. He was led by the Spirit into the desert. Sometimes for us the only way we know we are in the wilderness is once we are there!

The wilderness we experience may not be one of sand, heat or desolation; ours could be a period of loneliness and grief; or facing an uncertain future because of the loss of a job or waiting for a medical diagnosis. Or it might be the kind of wilderness that just lingers in the depths of your soul, where we wait and wait to hear a word from God, but all we hear is nothing but our own, slow heartbeat.

It is rarely of our choosing that we have these wilderness experiences, but they are all too common – and for some all too frequent – in our Christians lives. Does that mean that we've done something wrong or aren't quite living as we should? No!

We can echo David's words in Psalm 23. Even though I walk through the harshest of times, even there Jesus is with me. Just as he faced the reality and the harshness of the wilderness, he promises to be with us in ours. The word you're longing to hear from God was spoken by Jesus, for you today, 'I am with you, always, even now and even here.'

Lord, your ministry began in the wilderness. Be with us now. In the scorching hot days of our busyness, walk with us. In the freezing cold nights of our insecurity, lie beside us. God of the wilderness, be our friend. Amen

SANDRA WHEATLEY

Facing temptation

After fasting for forty days and forty nights, he was hungry. The tempter came to him. (NIV)

It is a hard fact of life that we face temptations of some sort every day of our lives. So today we revisit Jesus' time in the wilderness to see what we can learn from him.

I have no doubt that Jesus was 100% human. I also have no doubt that Jesus was 100% God. I was useless at maths at school and this calculation may not seem to add up, yet Jesus is truly a 200% person! In theology it is known as hypostatic union. He is one person with two distinct natures, both God and man.

And as Jesus the man, he faced every temptation: physically, in his hunger/appetite and need for food; emotionally, in whether God really would protect and save him; and finally the temptation to bypass the suffering and death on the cross to reign supreme over the kingdoms of the world.

Temptation isn't sin. It is an invitation. We sin when we accept the invitation and act on it.

The invitation comes in many guises to wrong-foot us into thinking that God doesn't care, doesn't understand, has abandoned us or doesn't see us. The temptations often come when we are at our most vulnerable, as Jesus was: when we're alone or hungry for food, for love or for understanding; hungry for power, something more, something better.

Satan seizes his moment and brings whispers of doubt that God cares. He suggests that God doesn't see; he doesn't know us – it's okay to try to go it alone.

If the temptation you're facing today has you in this 'corner', please read Hebrews 4:15. Jesus is *your* high priest and his promise to be with *you* is based on his having gone through all the temptations you're facing. Trust in his word for you today. He is with you.

Lord Jesus, my hight priest, I lean on you today. Please help and hold me. You know all that I face and how to bring me through. Thank you, Lord. Amen
SANDRA WHEATLEY

In our doubting

'Because you have seen me, you have believed; blessed are those who have not seen me and yet have believed.' (NIV)

I love it when the words Jesus spoke centuries ago include you and me in the here and now. We are the blessed ones who haven't seen Jesus and yet believe!

Thomas was so upfront and honest about his doubts concerning the appearance of Jesus to the other disciples. I wonder how he felt during the week before Jesus appeared again. Did faith and doubt coexist with Thomas? When Jesus and Thomas did finally meet, Jesus didn't castigate Thomas for doubting; he showed him his hands and his side, just as Thomas had wanted him to. 'My Lord and my God!' Thomas exclaimed.

Doubt is an uncomfortable word. Are we allowed to doubt? Are we seen as lacking in faith if we dare to tell others of the doubts we have? I have learned that doubt isn't the opposite or absence of faith, rather it is part of faith and often nurtures a growth in my faith. And yet it is at times of sorrow, disappointment or hurt that doubt can impact our faith and cause us to wonder if God really loves and cares for us.

There was another person Jesus encountered with doubts and he too wasn't condemned or dismissed. Mark 9:17–26 tells the story of a desperate father who brought his demon-possessed son to the disciples for healing. When Jesus told him that 'everything is possible for him who believes', it is the father's response that resounds in my heart too: 'I do believe; help me overcome my unbelief!' Jesus answered his plea. He still does.

If you are struggling with doubt and what to do, be as honest as the father and Thomas were with Jesus. Just as he was with them, Jesus will be with you. He'll meet with you where you are.

Lord Jesus, I do believe, help me overcome my unbelief. I know you can. I know you will. You are my Lord and my God. Amen

SANDRA WHEATLEY

An offer we can't refuse!

'Walk with me and work with me – watch how I do it. Learn the unforced rhythms of grace.' (MSG)

These verses have been such a refuge for me when tiredness and exhaustion have ground me down. Jesus' wonderful invitation – 'Come to me' – opens up such an opportunity to step aside from it all and be with him. It is an invitation that is open to everyone, especially the weary and burdened, the stressed, worried, exhausted and overwhelmed. We have a place to go, a soothing refuge in him.

Immediately he says he will give us rest. I have found two definitions of the 'rest' Jesus used: one is the 'cessation of labour' and the other is simply the relaxation of strings that have been pulled too tight. That sounds so familiar, doesn't it? Sometimes it takes a little while to stop and to cease from our labours or to let the over-pulled strings ease a little. This is no quick fix, as Jesus is once again inviting us to be with him. His way of doing things and his pace is often so different from ours. So, to enable us, Jesus offers us something which at first looks like a classic oxymoron, a yoke that is easy and a burden that is light!

We don't often see yokes on animals these days. They were designed for two animals to bring their strength together in order to pull a load that was impossible for one to pull alone. And one of the animals was often older and more experienced in yoke-bearing than the other, and so led the way and took more of the load – just as Jesus does. Being 'yoked' to him is a wonderful way to learn from him and to stay with him. And, as we do so, we realise that he is both *for* us and *with* us.

Father God, I'm tired and weary. I come to you and find rest in your presence and strength to carry on by your enabling grace. Thank you. Amen
SANDRA WHEATLEY

In our giving

'Truly I tell you, this poor widow has put more into the treasury than all the others.' (NIV)

During Holy Week, after a long day of being scrutinised and questioned, Jesus sits in the temple's Court of the Women. He does what I love to do, he 'people-watches'. Many rich people make a show of giving by throwing large amounts of money into the temple treasury, but it is one poor widow who catches Jesus' eye. She gave 'two very small copper coins, worth only a few pence', sometimes called a 'mite'. It was all she had. She left, unnoticed… except by Jesus.

Have you ever felt as if you have little to offer? At church we look around and see people who we think are more talented and gifted than us. They can sing better, speak more eloquently and run the groups at church without breaking into a sweat! Outside of church, too, we feel that we simply have nothing to offer because we don't feel good or able enough.

Within a few short years of being diagnosed with MS, I had lost my mobility and was about to lose my job and my home. As things worsened and I became more ill, despite the fervent prayers of my friends, my faith became suspect. It was a difficult time.

And yet my relationship with the Lord deepened in a way I could never have imagined. I could do little physically, but I'd learned what it was to 'soar on wings like eagles' (Isaiah 40:31). I could still pray for others throughout the day and, at times, all night – it was, and still is, such sweet communion. Life did still have worth and meaning. My 'two-coins' offering to God still mattered.

Yours does too. Your 'two-coins' have such worth and value to him. Jesus commends you, just as he commended the widow to the disciples.

Lord Jesus, may we bring whatever offerings we have today to you with the same attitude. This widow's 'mite' was her might. Amen

SANDRA WHEATLEY

In the darkest of times

The Lord turned and looked straight at Peter. Then Peter remembered the word the Lord had spoken to him. (NIV)

Peter's very public, very definite denial of knowing Jesus still makes stunning reading. After all Peter had said to Jesus during the last supper, he not once but three times denies knowing him. Was Peter aware that Jesus had heard him and seen him?

I have recently come across a picture illustrating Peter's denial, which my mum hung in our dining room not long after my family became Christians. It had been painted in such a way that Jesus' eyes seemed to follow you wherever you went in the room, and the verse today is its inscription. I was 11 at the time and used to find it comforting and unnerving all at the same time, depending on what mischief I'd been getting up to.

Peter will have known Jesus' 'look' so many times: that first day they met and Jesus called him to be a fisher of men; the compassion of Jesus' look as he healed his mum-in-law; and the look of delight as Peter walked on the water to meet him before he began to sink out of view.

There must have been so many times when Peter was encouraged to know Jesus' look. But now? Peter left the courtyard weeping bitterly as he denied knowing Jesus, his friend.

The 'I am with you' promise of Jesus reminds us that Jesus *is* with us every moment of every day. He heard Peter's denial just as he has heard many things that I so wish I hadn't said (or done). Jesus has looked straight into my life and I have remembered and wept bitterly too. But never once has it been a look of anger or condemnation, and I don't believe it was with Peter. For Peter there was forgiveness and reinstatement (John 21:15–19). There is for us too.

Lord Jesus, in those times when you look into my life and I remember the promises I've made and then broken, I'm sorry, Lord. Please forgive me and renew me by your grace. Amen.

SANDRA WHEATLEY

Every moment, every day... always

'And surely I am with you always, to the very end of the age'. (NIV)

Towards the end of 2019, news bulletins began to report that a new deadly virus was ravaging the city of Wuhan in China. Cases were increasing and the death rate was rising. Our TV screens showed pictures of deserted streets and hospitals being overrun with dying patients.

By March 2020, the virus had taken hold in the UK and we faced lockdown and shielding. The world had not been in the grip of such a pandemic for nearly a century.

Where was Jesus? What of his promise to be with us always, to the very end of the age?

Our churches closed their doors, but not their impact and influence. Christians were faced with the greatest challenge in a generation: to 'be Jesus' to our communities and families despite the huge restrictions of lockdown. Did you see him? Did he keep his promise?

He was there, just as he said he would be. He was the doctor and the nurse caring for those ravaged by the virus. He was the porter and the cleaner ensuring the hospitals were cleaned and safe. He was the teacher who continued to work to ensure key workers' children were safe and their work could continue. He was the shop assistant who worked hard to keep shops open for essential items. He was the bin worker collecting our rubbish and the carers in the homes of our elderly, frail parents. He was the neighbour who cooked meals. He was the friend who called on the phone to let us know we weren't forgotten. He was with us. He said he would be. Did you see him? I did.

Father God, the world has been ravaged by a virus we had no answer for. But in the midst of every crisis, every loss, every tragedy – you came. You were there. You are here. With us to the very end of the age. Thank you, Lord! Amen
SANDRA WHEATLEY

BRF Centenary Prayer

Gracious God,
We rejoice in this centenary year
that you have grown BRF
from a local network of Bible readers
into a worldwide family of ministries.
Thank you for your faithfulness
in nurturing small beginnings
into surprising blessings.
We rejoice that, from the youngest to the oldest,
so many have encountered your word
and grown as disciples of Christ.
Keep us humble in your service,
ambitious for your glory
and open to new opportunities.
For your name's sake
Amen

Enabling all ages to grow in faith

Anna Chaplaincy

Living Faith

Messy Church

Parenting for Faith

100 years of BRF

2022 is BRF's 100th anniversary! Look out for details of our special new centenary resources, a beautiful centenary rose and an online thanksgiving service that we hope you'll attend. This centenary year we're focusing on sharing the story of BRF, the story of the Bible – and we hope you'll share your stories of faith with us too.

Find out more at **brf.org.uk/centenary**.

To find out more about our work, visit

brf.org.uk

Sharing *the* Story *since* 1922

Recommended reading

This year's BRF Lent book explores: What is the Easter story really about, and how do we share it? Through each week of Lent, a different aspect of the Easter story is examined: repenting, changing, hoping, trusting, forgiving, loving and sacrificing. Within each week, the days are focused on what we need to do in order to share the story: listening, understanding, reflecting, living, telling, sharing and becoming. Each day offers a Bible passage, followed by a reflection and prayer activity.

Sharing the Easter Story
From reading to living the gospel
Sally Welch
978 1 80039 098 0 £8.99
brfonline.org.uk

Some women of the Hebrew scriptures are well known, but many others are barely remembered. Even when they are, we often don't pause on them long enough to think about what we might learn from them. *Unveiled*, written with frankness and humour and illustrated with striking artwork from a young artist, explores the stories of 40 women in 40 days. Each reflection ends with a short application to everyday life, guidance for further thought and a prayer.

Unveiled
Women of the Old Testament and the choices they made
Reflections by Clare Hayns, artwork by Micah Hayns
978 1 80039 072 0 £9.99
brfonline.org.uk

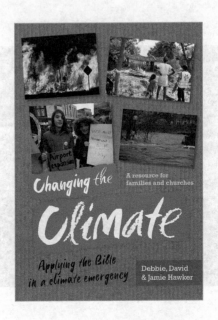

The climate crisis is one of the most important issues of our time, threatening lives and livelihoods. This workbook shows how the Bible is relevant to environmentalism, and how we can all play our part in limiting the negative effects of climate change. Each of the twelve chapters looks at a particular Bible passage, connects it with climate action, poses questions and suggests practical steps that can be taken.

Changing the Climate
Applying the Bible in a climate emergency
Debbie Hawker, David Hawker and Jamie Hawker
978 1 80039 022 5 £9.99
brfonline.org.uk

To order

Online: brfonline.org.uk
Telephone: +44 (0)1865 319700
Mon–Fri 9.30–17.00

Delivery times within the UK are
normally 15 working days. Prices are
correct at the time of going to press
but may change without prior notice.

Title	Price	Qty	Total
Sharing the Easter Story	£8.99		
Unveiled	£9.99		
Changing the Climate	£9.99		

POSTAGE AND PACKING CHARGES			
Order value	UK	Europe	Rest of world
Under £7.00	£2.00		
£7.00–£29.99	£3.00	Available on request	Available on request
£30.00 and over	FREE		

Total value of books	
Donation	
Postage and packing	
Total for this order	

Please complete in BLOCK CAPITALS

Title .... First name/initials .... Surname ....

Address ....

.... Postcode ....

Acc. No. .... Telephone ....

Email ....

Method of payment

☐ Cheque (made payable to BRF) ☐ MasterCard / Visa

Card no. ☐☐☐☐ ☐☐☐☐ ☐☐☐☐ ☐☐☐☐

Expires end ☐☐ ☐☐ Security code ☐☐☐ Last 3 digits on the reverse of the card

Signature .... Date ..../.........../..........

We will use your personal data to process this order. From time to time we may send you
information about the work of BRF. Please contact us if you wish to discuss your mailing
preferences **brf.org.uk/privacy**

Please return this form to:

BRF, 15 The Chambers, Vineyard, Abingdon OX14 3FE | **enquiries@brf.org.uk**
For terms and cancellation information, please visit **brfonline.org.uk/terms**.

Bible Reading Fellowship is a charity (233280) and company limited by guarantee (301324),
registered in England and Wales

DBDWG0122

SUBSCRIPTION INFORMATION

Each issue of *Day by Day with God* is available from Christian bookshops everywhere. Copies may also be available through your church book agent or from the person who distributes Bible reading notes in your church.

Alternatively you may obtain *Day by Day with God* on subscription direct from the publishers. There are two kinds of subscription:

Individual subscriptions
covering 3 issues for 4 copies or less, payable in advance (including postage & packing).

To order, please complete the details on page 144 and return with the appropriate payment to: BRF, 15 The Chambers, Vineyard, Abingdon OX14 3FE

You can also use the form on page 144 to order a gift subscription for a friend.

Group subscriptions
covering 3 issues for 5 copies or more, sent to one UK address (post free).

Please note that the annual billing period for group subscriptions runs from 1 May to 30 April.

To order, please complete the details on page 143 and return with the appropriate payment to: BRF, 15 The Chambers, Vineyard, Abingdon OX14 3FE

You will receive an invoice with the first issue of notes.

All our Bible reading notes can be ordered online by visiting
brfonline.org.uk/collections/subscriptions

Day by Day with God is also available as
an app for Android, iPhone and iPad
brfonline.org.uk/collections/apps

Follow us on Instagram: **@daybydaywithgod**

All subscription enquiries should be directed to:
BRF, 15 The Chambers, Vineyard, Abingdon OX14 3FE
+44 (0)1865 319700 | **enquiries@brf.org.uk**

DBDWG0122

DAY BY DAY WITH GOD GROUP SUBSCRIPTION FORM

All our Bible reading notes can be ordered online by visiting
brfonline.org.uk/collections/subscriptions

The group subscription rate for *Day by Day with God* will be £14.55 per person until April 2023.

☐ I would like to take out a group subscription for _____ (quantity) copies.

☐ Please start my order with the May 2022 / September 2022 / January 2023* issue. I would like to pay annually/receive an invoice* with each edition of the notes. (*delete as appropriate)

Please do not send any money with your order. Send your order to BRF and we will send you an invoice.

Name and address of the person organising the group subscription:

Title _____ First name/initials _____ Surname _____

Address_____

_____ Postcode _____

Telephone _____ Email _____

Church_____

Name and address of the person paying the invoice if the invoice needs to be sent directly to them:

Title _____ First name/initials _____ Surname _____

Address_____

_____ Postcode _____

Telephone _____ Email _____

We will use your personal data to process this order. From time to time we may send you information about the work of BRF. Please contact us if you wish to discuss your mailing preferences **brf.org.uk/privacy**

Please return this form to:
BRF, 15 The Chambers, Vineyard, Abingdon OX14 3FE | **enquiries@brf.org.uk**

For terms and cancellation information, please visit **brfonline.org.uk/terms**.

Bible Reading Fellowship is a charity (233280) and company limited by guarantee (301324), registered in England and Wales

To order online, please visit **brfonline.org.uk/collections/subscriptions**

☐ I would like to give a gift subscription (please provide both names and addresses)
☐ I would like to take out a subscription myself (complete your name and address details only once)

Title .... First name/initials .... Surname ....

Address ....

.... Postcode ....

Telephone .... Email ....

Gift subscription name ....

Gift subscription address ....

.... Postcode ....

Gift subscription (20 words max. or include your own gift card):

....

....

Please send *Day by Day with God* beginning with the May 2022 / September 2022 / January 2023 issue (*delete as appropriate*):

(*please tick box*)	UK	Europe	Rest of world
1-year subscription	☐ £18.30	☐ £26.25	☐ £30.15
2-year subscription	☐ £35.70	N/A	N/A

Optional donation to support the work of BRF £ ....

Total enclosed £ .... (cheques should be made payable to 'BRF')

Please charge my MasterCard / Visa with £ ....

Card no. ☐☐☐☐ ☐☐☐☐ ☐☐☐☐ ☐☐☐☐

Expires end ☐☐ ☐☐   Security code ☐☐☐   Last 3 digits on the reverse of the card

Signature .... Date ....../....../......

We will use your personal data to process this order. From time to time we may send you information about the work of BRF. Please contact us if you wish to discuss your mailing preferences **brf.org.uk/privacy**

Please return this form to:
BRF, 15 The Chambers, Vineyard, Abingdon OX14 3FE | enquiries@brf.org.uk
For terms and cancellation information, please visit **brfonline.org.uk/terms**.

Bible Reading Fellowship is a charity (233280) and company limited by guarantee (301324), registered in England and Wales

DBDWG0122